USSR Energy
Atlas

Central Intelligence Agency
January 1985

Preface

The USSR is the largest country in the world and the second-largest producer and consumer of energy. Its vast landmass and adjacent continental shelves contain enormous energy resources. Only in recent years, however, has the extent of the exploration and development of its fuel resources spanned the entire country.

A nationwide quest for new energy sources has rapidly outdated Soviet energy maps. Names like Samotlor, Fedorovo, Urengoy, Kansk-Achinsk, and Ekibastuz have become as well known to Soviet energy planners as Baku, Romashkino, Orenburg, and Donets were a decade or two ago. Likewise, the construction of oil and gas pipelines, electric transmission lines, roads, railroads, and towns has required extensive development of remote areas of Central Asia, Kazakhstan, Siberia, and the Far East.

Soviet energy is a strategic issue that transcends international boundaries. Soviet oil and gas exports have increasingly become available to Western buyers since the 1970s, and the Soviets also import large amounts of Western equipment and technology to upgrade the capabilities of the domestic energy industry.

This atlas uses a wide variety of information to portray many aspects of Soviet energy. Maps, graphics, photographs, and text provide a general understanding and appreciation of the major Soviet energy resources—oil, gas, coal, and primary electricity—as well as minor fuels and alternative energy sources.

GI 85-10001

This publication is prepared for the use of US Government officials, and the format, coverage, and content are designed to meet their specific requirements. US Government officials may obtain additional copies of this document directly or through liaison channels from the Central Intelligence Agency.

Requesters outside the US Government may obtain subscriptions to CIA publications similar to this one by addressing inquiries to:

Document Expediting (DOCEX) Project
Exchange and Gift Division
Library of Congress
Washington, D.C. 20540

or: National Technical Information Service
5285 Port Royal Road
Springfield, VA 22161

Requesters outside the US Government not interested in subscription service may purchase specific publications either in paper copy or microform from:

Photoduplication Service
Library of Congress
Washington, D.C. 20540

or: National Technical Information Service
5285 Port Royal Road
Springfield, VA 22161
(To expedite service call the
NTIS Order Desk—(703) 487-4650)

This publication may also be purchased from:

Superintendent of Documents
US Government Printing Office
Washington, D.C. 20402
Stock number 041-015-00157-4

Table of Contents

3

USSR: Energy Overview

The USSR is better endowed with energy resources than any other country in the world. It is the world's largest oil producer and has the largest oil reserves outside the Persian Gulf region. Soviet gas reserves are the largest in the world, and the USSR is also the world's leading gas producer. Coal resources are enormous, although most are unfavorably located at great distances from consuming centers. Electric power output, generated largely from thermal sources, ranks second to the United States.

Moscow's desire to maintain steady economic growth requires an expanding energy resource development program as reflected in the 11th Five-Year Plan (1981-85). The focus of the current effort is to continue the expansion of West Siberian oil and gas development, accelerate nuclear power plant construction in the European USSR, and further exploit vast Central Siberian coal resources. In addition, the Soviets hope to increase the efficient use of these primary fuels through new programs for energy conservation and fuel substitution.

Energy exports are the principal source of Soviet hard currency earnings. Revenues from exports to Western countries permit the acquisition of equipment and technology for a variety of Soviet activities; particularly important are energy efforts to increase oil recovery, transport natural gas, and exploit offshore energy resources.

Energy investment is surging as the Soviets attempt to meet growing energy demand through investments in new production areas and maintenance and enhancement of production from established regions. Costs are rising as exploration and production move into the more remote eastern regions of the USSR and operating conditions become more difficult.

Oil and gas exploration in Tyumen' Oblast, West Siberia.

Construction of nuclear power reactor in the Ukrainian SSR.

Foreign equipment being used to mine Central Siberian brown coal.

Offshore drilling technology is acquired from energy export revenues.

Domestic and International Issues

Energy Decisionmaking

The driving force behind Soviet energy policy is Moscow's desire to remain self-sufficient in energy while increasing hard currency earnings from energy exports. As the Soviets themselves have often noted, "The Soviet Union is currently the only highly developed country in the world meeting all of its own fuel and energy needs from its own resources." In 1983 the Central Committee of the Communist Party of the Soviet Union (CPSU) adopted a long-range energy program that provides guidelines for energy resource development and exploitation until the year 2000. Its emphasis is on: attaining an optimal energy mix through substitution of natural gas, nuclear power, and coal for oil; developing new sources of energy, such as geothermal, solar, wind, and tidal; improving and expanding the energy infrastructure; continuing the development of oil and gas in West Siberia and their transport to the European part of the country; and increasing fuel and energy conservation by means of technological improvements and improved utilization of existing resources.

Kremlin Palace of Congresses, Moscow.

Responsibility for energy matters in the USSR is shared among a number of key party and government organizations. The Politburo of the CPSU, the highest decisionmaking body in the USSR, determines the country's basic energy research, development, and production policies. In the face of severe problems, the Politburo can act unilaterally to redirect energy policy or shift the allocation of resources necessary for its implementation. Much of the formulation of these energy policies actually occurs in the Presidium of the Council of Ministers, the Secretariat of the Central Committee of the CPSU, and the USSR State Planning Committee (Gosplan). These three groups advise the Politburo, provide guidance on energy policy and management to lower levels, and collectively serve as a high-level forum for discussions of alternative strategies. Like the Politburo, they are concerned with integrating energy policy into a broader economic and political framework.

A significant contribution to the decisionmaking process is made by the state committees and ministries directly involved in implementing energy policies. These organizations possess a level of technical expertise that is largely missing at higher levels. They provide assessments of resource issues and production capabilities and give continuity to energy policies.

Energy Decisionmaking in the Soviet Union

Politburo of the CPSU

Secretariat of the CPSU Central Committee

Presidium of USSR Council of Ministers

USSR Academy of Sciences

Energy-Related Committees

State Committee for Science and Technology (GKNT)	State Planning Committee (Gosplan)	State Committee for Useful Mineral Reserves (GKZ)	State Committee for the Supply of Petroleum Products	State Committee for Utilization of Atomic Power (GKAE)	State Committee to Supervise Work Safety in the Atomic Power Industry

Energy-Related Ministries

Geology	Petroleum Industry	Gas Industry	Chemical and Petroleum Machine Building	Construction of Petroleum and Gas Industry Enterprises	Petroleum Refining and Petrochemical Industry

Coal Industry	Power and Electrification	Power Machine Building	Electrical Equipment Industry

Ministries Involved in Support for Energy

Construction	Finance	Foreign Trade	Installation and Special Construction Work	Land Reclamation and Water Resources	Railways

Organizations With Primary Responsibility for Energy Production and Management

USSR Academy of Sciences. Oversees research on new energy sources and development of new methods of energy resource production.

Energy-Related Committees

State Committee for Science and Technology (GKNT) (A-U).[a] Sets energy research and development priorities; evaluates research and development proposals from the Academy of Sciences and the production ministries; assists in acquisition of foreign technology; administers scientific and technical exchanges with foreign countries.

State Planning Committee (Gosplan) (U-R). Coordinates five-year plans in all fields, including energy; makes and oversees plans for energy-related departments, including geology and mineral resources, coal, petroleum and gas industries, power and electrification, and transport; serves as a consultant on energy policy.

State Committee for Useful Mineral Reserves (GKZ) (A-U). Reviews geologic data from exploratory wells to certify reserves and reservoir properties; establishes coefficients of extraction (rates of recovery) for petroleum and condensate; classifies petroleum and gas reserves; has final approval for field drilling plans submitted by Ministry of the Petroleum Industry; maintains reserve stocks of petroleum and fuels.

State Committee for the Supply of Petroleum Products (U-R). Oversees the procurement, storage, and distribution of petroleum products including those destined for export; administers petroleum pipelines and storage bases; monitors industrial use of petroleum products.

State Committee for the Utilization of Atomic Power (GKAE) (A-U). Administers civilian atomic energy programs; conducts joint research projects with foreign countries.

State Committee To Supervise Work Safety in the Atomic Power Industry (A-U). Establishes and enforces standards for nuclear power plant safety and radioactive waste disposal.

Energy-Related Ministries

Ministry of Geology (U-R). Conducts exploration for new oil, gas, and coal deposits; monitors contracts with foreign firms for energy resource exploration in USSR; directs development of new prospecting techniques, equipment, and methods of mineral analysis.

Ministry of the Petroleum Industry (A-U). Manages production drilling, extraction, transportation, and sales of petroleum; shares responsibility with Ministry of Geology for exploratory petroleum drilling and extraction and processing of gas condensate.

Ministry of the Gas Industry (A-U). Oversees the extraction, processing, underground storage, and transportation of natural gas from established fields; directs offshore oil and gas exploratory drilling and production; participates in onshore gas exploration, gas condensate processing, and geothermal energy production.

Ministry of Chemical and Petroleum Machine Building (A-U). Oversees the manufacture and supply of extraction and production equipment to the petroleum, gas, and petrochemical industries.

Ministry of Construction of Petroleum and Gas Industry Enterprises (A-U). Constructs petroleum and gas pipelines and field processing plants; has primary responsibility for compressor station construction.

Ministry of the Petroleum Refining and Petrochemical Industry (U-R). Oversees all aspects of petroleum refining and petrochemical processing, as well as the production of synthetic rubber, aromatic hydrocarbons, lubricants, fuels, liquid paraffins, chemical feed additives, and chemical reagents for enhanced oil recovery.

Ministry of the Coal Industry (U-R). Manages coal and oil shale extraction and equipment production; participates in the development of technologies for solid fuel liquefaction and gasification.

Ministry of Power and Electrification (U-R). Directs the design, construction, operation, and maintenance of hydroelectric, thermal, and atomic power plants; participates in tidal, solar, geothermal, and wind energy production as well as research and development of techniques for solid fuel liquefaction and gasification.

Ministry of Power Machine Building (A-U). Provides heavy equipment for thermal, nuclear, and hydroelectric power stations; manufactures gas turbines, pumps, and superchargers for pipeline compressor stations and heat recovery equipment for the petroleum refining industry; operates the nuclear reactor manufacturing plants located in Volgodonsk and Kolpino.

Ministry of the Electrical Equipment Industry (A-U). Directs research, development, and manufacture of electrical generation and distribution equipment.

Ministries Involved in Support for Energy

Ministry of Construction (U-R). Performs basic construction for energy production industries.

Ministry of Finance (U-R). Allocates financial resources for energy production, research, and development.

Ministry of Foreign Trade (A-U). Oversees trade in petroleum, gas, and coal products, as well as energy resource extraction, processing, and transportation equipment.

Ministry of Installation and Special Construction Work (U-R). Constructs installations and buildings for the coal, petroleum, and nuclear power industries; assists in construction of refineries, pipelines, and drilling rigs; conducts some drilling and blasting work.

Ministry of Land Reclamation and Water Resources (U-R). Participates in construction of hydroelectric plants, in the control of pollution from thermal power plants, and in the management of windpower facilities; also involved in construction of petroleum and gas pipelines.

Ministry of Railways (A-U). Transports coal, petroleum products, and other fuels.

[a] All-Union (A-U) organizations have no regional counterparts; union republic (U-R) organizations operate locally through corresponding organizations on the republic level.

Energy Balances

The Soviet Union produces nearly one-fifth of the world's primary energy and is currently the leading energy exporter and the largest producer of oil and natural gas. The USSR is third after the United States and China in coal production.

Domestic production accounts for 99 percent of total Soviet energy use; imports are more a matter of geographic convenience than necessity. The USSR consumes approximately 85 percent of the primary energy it produces and relies on oil, gas, and coal for the bulk of its energy needs.

The overall production rate of primary energy, after expanding rapidly for two decades, has slowed considerably during the early 1980s. The 4.5-percent annual growth rate of the 1970s dropped to about 2.5 percent a year during 1981-82. Soviet plan goals suggest that this slower rate may continue during the remainder of the 11th Five-Year Plan. In addition to the depletion of the most easily exploitable reserves, the slower rate of production is because of inadequate technology and equipment, insufficient capital investment in some sectors of the energy industry, and poor logistic coordination of materials and supplies.

The Energy Mix

Production of major fuels (oil, natural gas, and coal) accounts for more than 90 percent of the Soviet energy mix. Oil production has begun to level off after three decades of steady growth. Output in 1983 was 12.33 million barrels per day (b/d), just 300,000 b/d more than in 1980. The production of natural gas, important both as a substitute for oil domestically and as a source of hard currency export revenues, has experienced impressive growth since 1970. Gas output rose from 3.3 million b/d oil equivalent in 1970 to 8.9 million b/d oil equivalent in 1983. Coal output, although increasing 28 percent since 1960 in terms of energy content, continues to comprise a decreasing share of primary energy production.

The shares of different fuels in total Soviet energy consumption have also shifted significantly over the past two decades. Whereas natural gas provided only 8 percent of Soviet energy requirements in 1960, it accounted for 29 percent in 1982. During the same period, oil's share rose from 24 to 37 percent. This growth in oil and gas occurred at the expense of coal. In 1960 the Soviets relied on coal for more than one-half of their total energy needs; in 1982 it provided only 26 percent.

World: Oil, Gas, and Coal Production

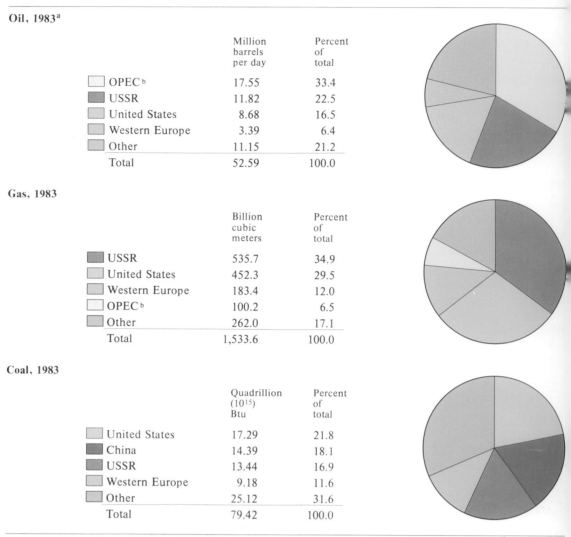

Oil, 1983[a]

	Million barrels per day	Percent of total
OPEC[b]	17.55	33.4
USSR	11.82	22.5
United States	8.68	16.5
Western Europe	3.39	6.4
Other	11.15	21.2
Total	52.59	100.0

Gas, 1983

	Billion cubic meters	Percent of total
USSR	535.7	34.9
United States	452.3	29.5
Western Europe	183.4	12.0
OPEC[b]	100.2	6.5
Other	262.0	17.1
Total	1,533.6	100.0

Coal, 1983

	Quadrillion (10[15]) Btu	Percent of total
United States	17.29	21.8
China	14.39	18.1
USSR	13.44	16.9
Western Europe	9.18	11.6
Other	25.12	31.6
Total	79.42	100.0

[a] Excludes natural gas liquids.

[b] Includes Algeria, Ecuador, Gabon, Indonesia, Iran, Iraq, Kuwait, Libya, Nigeria, Qatar, Saudi Arabia, Venezuela, and United Arab Emirates

Source: Energy Information Administration, US Department of Energy.

USSR: Primary Energy

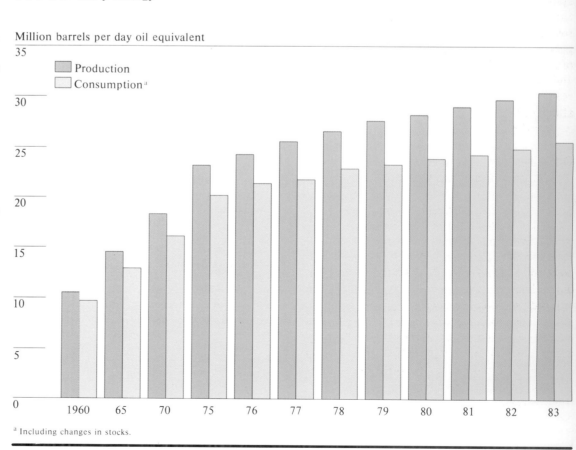

Million barrels per day oil equivalent

- Production
- Consumption[a]

[a] Including changes in stocks.

USSR: Energy Balances

Million barrels per day oil equivalent

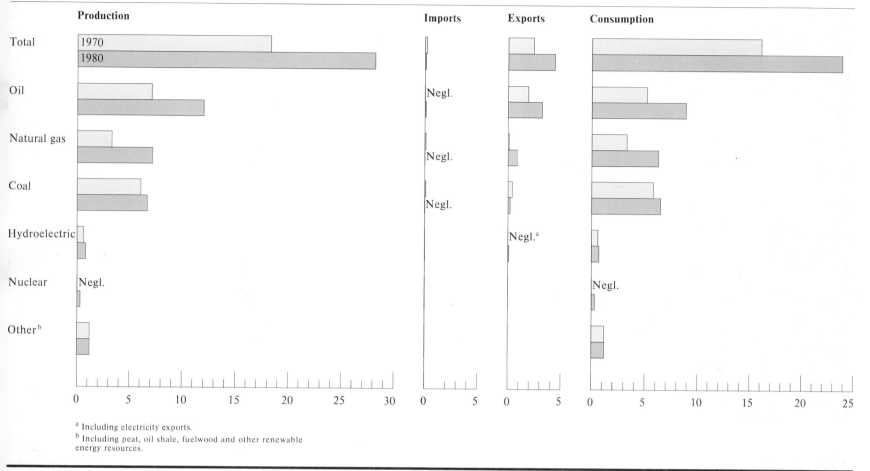

Million barrels per day oil equivalent

Production — Imports — Exports — Consumption

Total: 1970, 1980
Oil — Negl.
Natural gas — Negl.
Coal — Negl.
Hydroelectric — Negl.[a]
Nuclear — Negl. — Negl.
Other[b]

0 5 10 15 20 25 30 | 0 5 | 0 5 | 0 5 10 15 20 25

[a] Including electricity exports.
[b] Including peat, oil shale, fuelwood and other renewable energy resources.

Conservation and Substitution

Rising costs of energy production have led, as in the West, to a growing interest in curbing demand through conservation. But by most standards, the Soviet economy remains energy inefficient. Many of the barriers to improving energy efficiency are endemic to the Soviet system. Centralized planning and resource allocation, artificially low energy prices, and incentives geared toward meeting quantitative output goals do not reward innovation or efficient use of resources. Moreover, despite official goals and pronouncements about saving energy, the requisite capital and other resources have been allocated to energy production rather than conservation.

One of the best opportunities the Soviets have for reducing the growth of oil demand is by substituting natural gas for oil in electric power plants and large boilers. Such a program requires the construction of long-distance natural gas transmission pipelines, conversion of older plants to burn gas, completion of new gas-fired power plants, and expansion of lateral gas distribution lines and storage facilities. Aside from reduced use of oil in power plants and industrial boilers, the prospects for substitution are limited. Oil use for transportation and agriculture is not readily amenable to gas substitution, so that efforts to hold down oil use in these sectors of the economy must depend largely on conservation.

USSR: Electricity Balances

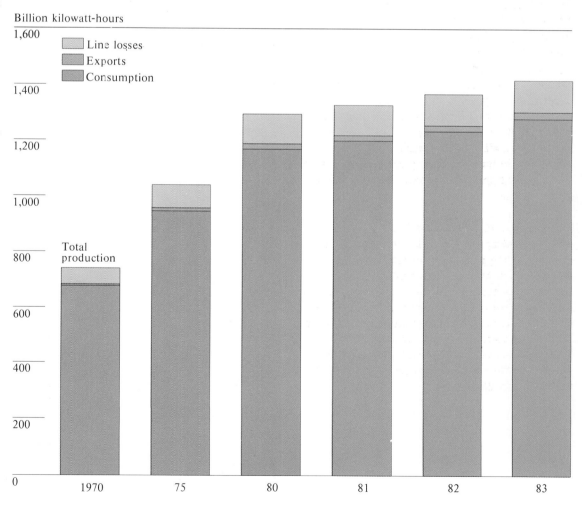

Billion kilowatt-hours

- Line losses
- Exports
- Consumption

Total production

1,600
1,400
1,200
1,000
800
600
400
200
0

1970 — 75 — 80 — 81 — 82 — 83

7

Foreign Markets

For most of the past decade, Soviet earnings from energy exports have been increasing, partly as a result of rising prices for oil and gas. The recent expansion of Soviet exports to the West has been responsible for important increases in hard currency earnings necessary for the development of new energy resources. The Soviets have used much of the new revenue to purchase Western equipment and technology for oil and gas exploration and production.

Although Soviet increases in oil exports to Council for Mutual Economic Assistance (CEMA) partners have slowed in recent years, the continuation of a steady flow of energy resources to Eastern Europe and Cuba remains a high priority for Moscow. Except for Romania and Poland, CEMA countries are dependent on the USSR for large shares of their energy supplies.

Hard Currency

Before the 1973 Arab oil embargo, Soviet hard currency earnings from energy exports comprised only 20 percent of the USSR's total yearly commodity export earnings. Some 85 to 90 percent of these energy-derived earnings came from oil. By 1977 the share of hard currency earned from oil and gas sales to the West had grown to more than 50 percent. In 1981 a soft world oil market forced the Soviets to reduce exports and temporarily settle for diminished earnings. Nevertheless, in 1982 Moscow achieved a record 28-percent increase in oil exports to non-Communist customers, largely through restrictions on deliveries to soft currency customers.

Oil continues to be the most important source of hard currency earnings for Moscow, but natural gas trade with the West is growing. In 1975 gas provided only 3 percent of hard currency earnings, but by 1982 natural gas earnings had risen to almost 14 percent of the total. The Soviets anticipate even greater increases in revenues from natural gas exports with the large-scale gas deliveries through the new Siberia–to–Western Europe pipeline.

Trading Partners

CEMA

For nearly two decades, the USSR has been the principal supplier of energy for its East European CEMA allies, Cuba, and Vietnam. During the 1970s the Soviets provided as much as three-fourths of the oil consumed by the East Europeans and almost all of the crude oil used by the Cubans. Most—though not all—of these sales were soft currency or barter deals. To help ease the economic burden of oil price increases, Moscow delayed raising the price of oil to its CEMA partners. Thus, for a number of years after OPEC's sharp price increases in the 1970s, the economies of the Soviet allies benefited from below-world-market prices. During this time, however, the Soviet Union kept encouraging its CEMA partners to reduce their dependence on oil and increase consumption of substitutes such as gas, coal, and nuclear energy. Moscow also took steps, including a five-year-moving-average pricing formula, to discourage future increases in East European imports of Soviet oil unless the extra oil was purchased with hard currency. Finally, in 1982 the Soviets began an actual cutback in oil deliveries to some CEMA members.

Historically, the Soviet Union and the East European CEMA members have worked closely to develop Soviet energy resources. Thus far, the gas pipeline from the Orenburg field, also known as the Soyuz (Union or Alliance) pipeline and completed in 1978, has been their largest joint project. The East Europeans provided labor, equipment, and hard currency support in exchange for future supplies of natural gas.

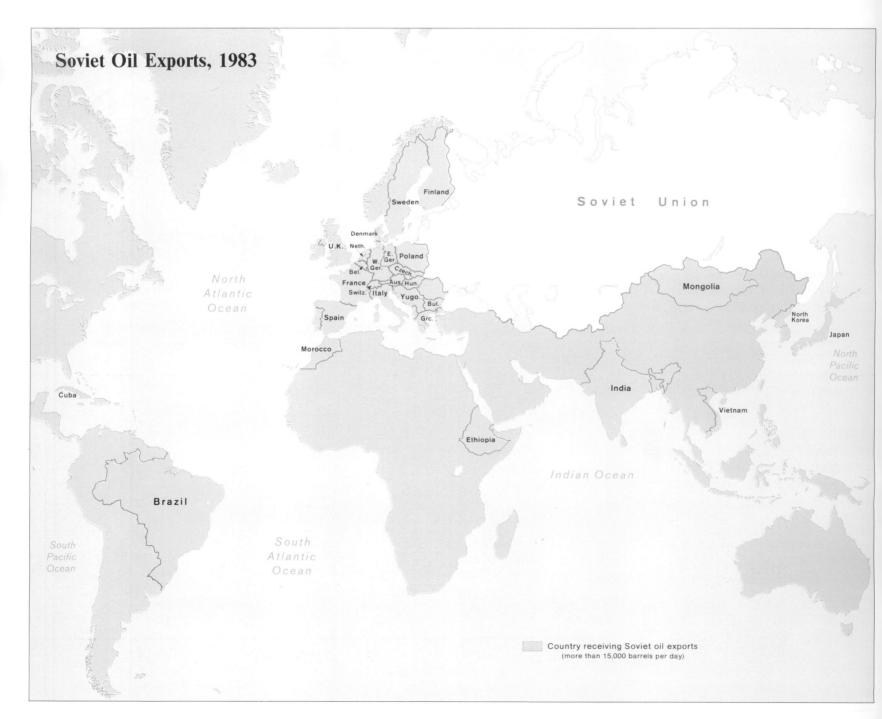

Soviet Oil Exports, 1983

Country receiving Soviet oil exports
(more than 15,000 barrels per day)

The production of Soviet nuclear reactors has also involved substantial East European cooperation. A recent agreement between these countries and the USSR calls for the other CEMA countries to specialize in the production of Soviet-designed reactor components to be used in an integrated electrical power system. The increased nuclear power capacity of the Soviet Union and the joint USSR-CEMA projects now under way to improve and enlarge the power transmission system should significantly increase Soviet capability to export electricity in the future.

Cuba, with limited domestic oil resources, has been heavily dependent on the Soviets for virtually all of its petroleum needs. The construction of a Soviet-designed nuclear power station in Cuba will improve Cuban energy self-sufficiency and decrease reliance on Moscow for oil.

Western Europe

Soviet energy trade with Western Europe was limited until the mid-1970s. Since then, the share of sales from the principal exported commodities, oil and gas, has become increasingly important. Currently, the Soviet Union's largest West European energy customers are West Germany, France, Italy, Austria, Belgium, the Netherlands, United Kingdom, Sweden, and Finland.

Between 1978 and 1981, the rapid growth in oil sales to Western Europe came to an abrupt halt as conservation efforts—"aided" by an oil-fueled recession—by the West Europeans started to take hold. Beginning in 1982 the Soviets partially compensated for the reduced hard currency earnings from long-term contracts by increasing their spot market sales of oil at major West European oil terminals.

In the mid-1970s the West Europeans turned to the Soviet Union in an effort to diversify their energy sources. Existing gas contracts from the late 1960s were expanded. This also led to a number of new joint projects, of which the most notable is the Siberia–to–Western Europe natural gas pipeline. The terms of many of these contracts usually include compensation agreements, involving either a form of barter, counterpurchase, or product payback arrangements,

in which future sales or delivery of a Soviet product are linked to an advance sale or delivery of Western equipment or technology. In exchange for providing technological help in constructing the Soviet gas pipeline system, the Europeans receive guaranteed supplies of natural gas.

Japan

Energy trade with Japan will play an important role in the development of East Siberian resources. Joint Soviet-Japanese development of Sakhalin Island oil and gas and of East Siberian coal reserves is now under way. Progress has been slow, however, as a result of financial problems and harsh climatic conditions. Currently, Japan is the primary hard currency importer of Soviet coking coal.

In addition to the hard currency, technology has been a significant part of Soviet-Japanese energy trade negotiations. The Japanese are a major supplier of energy technology; Soviet purchases account for approximately 15 percent of Japanese energy equipment and technology exports.

USSR: Hard Currency Exports

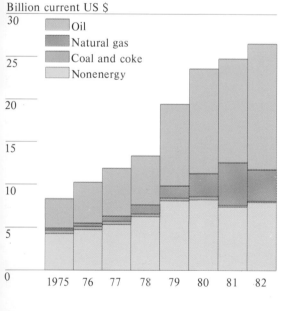

Billion current US $

Oil
Natural gas
Coal and coke
Nonenergy

1975 76 77 78 79 80 81 82

USSR: Oil Exports

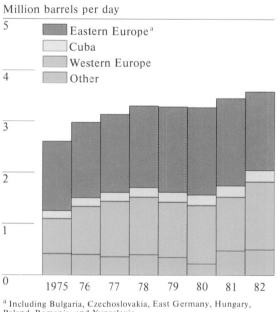

Million barrels per day

Eastern Europe[a]
Cuba
Western Europe
Other

1975 76 77 78 79 80 81 82

[a] Including Bulgaria, Czechoslovakia, East Germany, Hungary, Poland, Romania, and Yugoslavia.

USSR: Natural Gas Exports

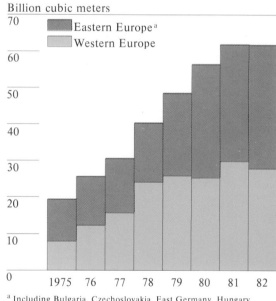

Billion cubic meters

Eastern Europe[a]
Western Europe

1975 76 77 78 79 80 81 82

[a] Including Bulgaria, Czechoslovakia, East Germany, Hungary, Poland, Romania, and Yugoslavia.

USSR: Energy Production Exported

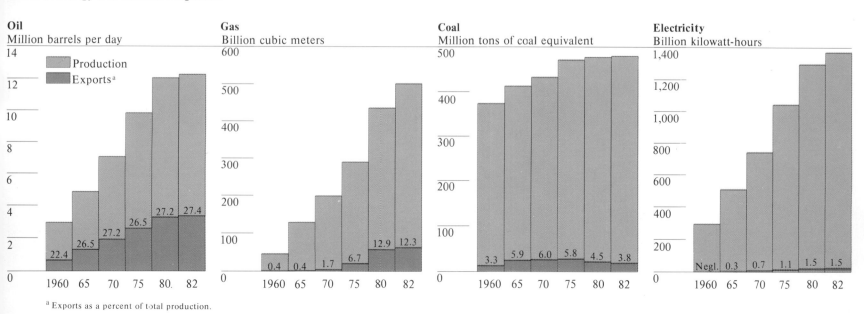

Oil
Million barrels per day

Production
Exports[a]

22.4 26.5 27.2 26.5 27.2 27.4

1960 65 70 75 80 82

Gas
Billion cubic meters

0.4 0.4 1.7 6.7 12.9 12.3

1960 65 70 75 80 82

Coal
Million tons of coal equivalent

3.3 5.9 6.0 5.8 4.5 3.8

1960 65 70 75 80 82

Electricity
Billion kilowatt-hours

Negl. 0.3 0.7 1.1 1.5 1.5

1960 65 70 75 80 82

[a] Exports as a percent of total production.

International Energy Projects

During the 1970s the Soviet Union entered into several foreign contract negotiations associated with domestic energy development. The principal motivation for these cooperative international ventures was Soviet desire to increase hard currency earnings and to acquire essential Western technology and equipment necessary for resource development. Of the many cooperative ventures negotiated with Western countries, three projects—the Siberia–to–Western Europe natural gas pipeline, the South Yakutia coal project, and Sakhalin oil and gas development—have recently received considerable worldwide publicity.

Two widely publicized liquefied natural gas (LNG) projects of the mid-1970s were the North Star project to ship Urengoy gas to the US east coast and the joint USSR-US-Japanese venture to develop Yakutia gas. Although both projects have lost US support, the Japanese still have some interest in Yakutia gas development.

Siberia–to–Western Europe Natural Gas Pipeline

The Siberia–to–Western Europe natural gas pipeline is the largest international trade project the Soviets have undertaken to date. Negotiations for the pipeline began in 1979, and Moscow signed gas purchase agreements in late 1981 with West German and French utilities, in June 1982 with Austria's Ferngas, and in May 1984 with Italy. Included in the pipeline negotiations were contracts for Soviet purchases of large-diameter pipe, turbine compressors, and related equipment from the major West European countries and Japan. Installation of the pipeline in the Soviet section was completed in September 1983; all compressors were to be in place in 1984. Plans call for partial deliveries of gas to start in 1984 and full deliveries to begin in 1987.

The Soviet Union has been exporting gas to Western Europe since the early 1970s. Between 1968 and 1975 Moscow concluded several "gas for pipe" agreements with Austria, France, Italy, and West Germany. Under these agreements, the USSR purchased large quantities of large-diameter pipe and other gas-related equipment with long-term, government-backed credits. To repay the loans and earn foreign exchange, the USSR contracted for long-term deliveries of natural gas to Western Europe.

The USSR will be able to use a combination of the existing Soyuz (Orenburg) pipeline, domestic trunklines, and East European transit lines to supplement the initial throughput of the export pipeline which began in early 1984. With the completion of the new 32-billion-cubic-meter-capacity export pipeline, total Soviet deliveries to Western Europe eventually could reach 60 billion cubic meters per year. They were almost 29 billion cubic meters in 1983.

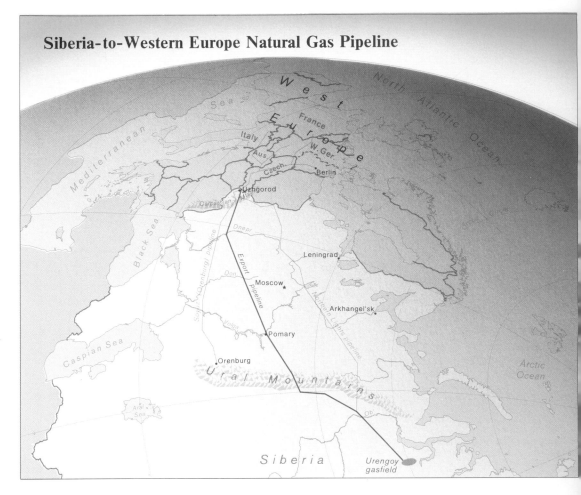

Siberia-to-Western Europe Natural Gas Pipeline

Imported large-diameter pipe sections at Leningrad port.

Pipe sections are transported by trucks from railyards to the construction site.

Soviet-made excavator being used to dig pipeline trench.

Pipe sections being welded by manual, arc-welding technique.

Welded pipe is coated, wrapped, and positioned within the prepared trench.

Concrete blocks are used in areas of swamp and permafrost to support the pipeline.

The Pipeline Route

Geographically, the Soviet portion of the pipeline runs 4,451 kilometers from Urengoy in the northern portion of the West Siberian basin to Uzhgorod at the Czechoslovak border. The pipeline route traverses some 700 kilometers of swamp and marshland, 2,000 kilometers of forest, and 550 kilometers of rocky terrain including the Ural and Carpathian mountain ranges. The construction route also crosses nearly 600 rivers and streams including the Ob' in West Siberia and the Volga, Don, and Dnepr in European USSR. The 2.5-kilometer Volga River crossing is the widest waterway on the route.

In the European USSR, the pipeline route crosses several of the country's most heavily populated and industrialized regions. Interconnecting the region's existing gas pipeline network with the export pipeline enables the Soviets to better respond to changing demand for gas.

Sakhalin Oil and Gas Project

The USSR reached a general agreement with Japan in 1975 for the joint development of Sakhalin's offshore petroleum resources. The agreement calls for SODECO—a consortium of Japanese petroleum and trading companies and one US firm, Gulf Oil—to finance the exploration and development of the offshore reserves through credits extended by Japan's Export-Import Bank. In return, SODECO is to receive Soviet oil and gas at preferential prices.

The joint Soviet-Japanese venture to exploit Sakhalin offshore oil resources is similar in many respects to the Siberia–to–Western Europe natural gas pipeline project. It includes the purchase of Western petroleum equipment financed through credits guaranteed by Western governments in exchange for Soviet repayment through the transfer of energy resources. In addition, the project will boost Soviet hard currency earnings.

Moscow will also acquire offshore experience and technology that could be extremely useful should the Soviets begin intensive exploitation of the potentially rich hydrocarbon deposits of the Barents and Kara Seas. The Sakhalin project will give the Japanese an opportunity to further diversify their oil and gas sources.

Work on the Sakhalin project has not met the projected plans. Exploration, already hampered by the short, ice-free drilling season, has also been delayed by equipment shortages and decisions to drill convenient but unproductive structures. Thus far, two fields—Odoptu and Chayvo—have been discovered off the northeast coast of Sakhalin Island.

South Yakutia Coal Project

A third major Soviet energy development facilitated by international investment and cooperation is the South Yakutia coal project. Terms of this cooperative venture with Japan, which began in 1975, call for the Japanese to receive specified percentages of the 9 million metric tons of annual coking coal production as repayment for their financial and technical investment.

The first stage of the South Yakutia coal project includes development of the Neryungri strip mine, installation and operation of imported mining equipment, a coal concentration facility to treat exported coal, and the first section of the Neryungri Thermal Power Station, where the first 210-MW generator started up in late 1983. The project, made possible by the construction of the Bamovskaya-Tynda-Berkakit (Little BAM) railroad, is scheduled for completion in 1985, nearly two years behind schedule. Limited coal production began in late 1978 when the Little BAM reached the mine. Production has grown from 400,000 tons in 1979 to more than 5 million tons in 1983.

The Soviets are hopeful the new Siberian town of Neryungri, in addition to being the major industrial city and energy hub of the South Yakutia region, will become one of the largest industrial complexes in Eastern Siberia. Because of the high quality of Yakutia's coking coal and the availability of nearby Aldan iron ore deposits, Neryungri is also being considered as a possible location for steel manufacture.

The Pipeline at a Glance

Length	4,451 kilometers (Urengoy-Uzhgorod)
Capacity	32 billion cubic meters per year
Pipe	2.7 million tons, 1,420-mm diameter
Operating pressure	75 atmospheres
Compressor stations	41 (40 with three 25-MW gas-turbine compressors each; one with five 10-MW gas-turbine compressors)
Total cost	$22 billion ($7 billion in hard currency)
Completion	1983 (pipelaying) 1984 (compressor stations)

Sakhalin Oil and Gas Region

South Yakutia Coal Region

Fuel Resources

Until recently, the Soviet Union has been able to find, extract, transport, and process its vast fuel resources at a rate sufficient to support rapid economic growth. But, beginning in the late 1970s, supplies of oil and coal, which together contribute nearly two-thirds of Soviet primary energy production, have suffered setbacks. Energy costs are rising because of the growing remoteness and lower quality of the newly discovered resources. Reports of fuel shortages and a growing energy conservation campaign attest to growing fuel supply problems. A current slowdown in the growth rate of oil production, uncertainty about the future world market for natural gas despite long-term contracts with the West Europeans, and stagnating coal output are major causes of concern for Soviet energy planners.

Historically, the large urban and industrial centers west of the Urals were almost totally dependent on plentiful nearby fuel resources. These western resources now provide only about 50 percent of the energy needs of the European USSR; the rest come from newly discovered reserves in Central Asia, Kazakhstan, the Urals, and Siberia. Although the Soviets have significant oil, gas, and coal resources in these southern and eastern regions, with the exception of natural gas they have been unable to develop them fast enough to keep pace with the expanding economy and replace the rapidly depleting and more accessible reserves near the consuming centers of the European USSR. Development of these new energy resources has been slow for a variety of reasons, ranging from the need for specialized equipment and technology to the requirement for enormous additional investment. Additionally, geographic constraints—climate, terrain, and distance—have compounded the problems associated with exploiting and transporting these resources.

The Soviet system of reserve classification for both major and minor fuel resources is very different from that used in the West. The Soviet reserve categories—A, B, C_1, C_2, D_1, and D_2—are based primarily on the degree of exploration and delineation drilling that has been carried out and cannot be directly equated to the Western categories of proved, probable, and possible reserves, which are based on prevailing economic and technological factors.

Overhead view of mobile jack-up drilling platform, Okha, near Sakhalin Island.

USSR/US: Reserves of Major Fuels, Yearend 1983[a]

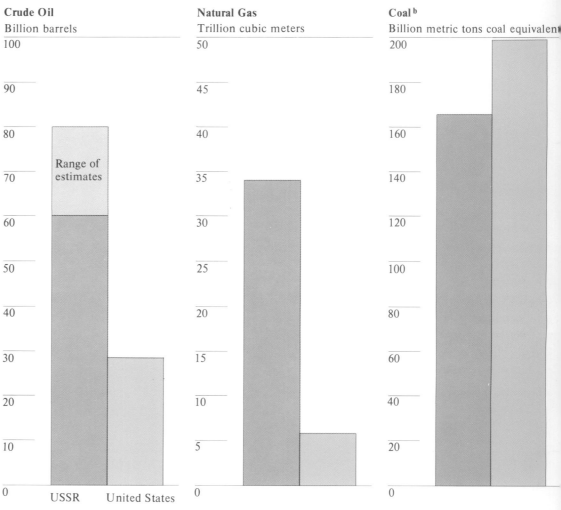

[a] The portion of total resources assessed as exploitable under local economic conditions and available technology.
[b] Yearend 1980.

Soviet Union: Reserve Classification System

Soviet Reserve Classification	Western Reserve Classification
Explored/Commercial Reserves $A + B + 30\%$ of C_1	Proved
A	
B	
C_1 (30%)	
	Probable
Prospective Reserves The remaining 70% of C_1 plus $C_2 + D_1 + D_2$	
C_1 (70%)	
	Possible
C_2	
D_1	
D_2	

"A" Category
- Geologically and geophysically examined in detail
- Delineated by exploration and production over the whole deposit
- Engineering data demonstrate recoverability
- Represent reserves in current production

"B" Category
- Geologically and geophysically examined in detail
- Evaluated by drilling to a degree adequate for development planning
- Engineering data demonstrate recoverability
- Represent on-hold reserves or unused producing capacity

"C_1" Category
- Represent reserves adjacent to "A" and "B" categories
- Geologically and geophysically evaluated
- Verified by minimal drilling
- Engineering data demonstrate partial recoverability, and average 30 percent will shift to "B" and then "A" categories

"C_2" Category
- Presumed to exist, based on favorable geologic and geophysical data analogous to that for areas containing verified reserves
- Some will shift to higher categories

"D_1" Category
- Speculative reserves presumed to exist on the basis of geologic analogy to reference areas
- Some will shift to "C_2" category

"D_2" Category
- Speculative reserves presumed to exist on the basis of geologic analogy to reference area
- Less geologically and geophysically evaluated than "D_1" category
- Some will shift to "D_1" category

Proved
Reserves which geological and engineering or drilling data demonstrate to be recoverable under existing economic and operating conditions

Probable
Incompletely defined reserves estimated to occur:
- In known producing areas
- As extensions of endowed areas
- In undiscovered areas within known resource-bearing geologic trends
- Recoverable under existing economic and operating conditions

Possible
Inferred reserves estimated to occur:
- In undiscovered areas analogous to other known resource-bearing areas
- Recoverable under existing economic and operating conditions

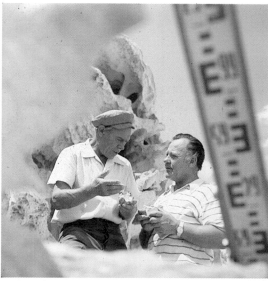

Oil and gas exploration on Mangyshlak Peninsula, North Caspian.

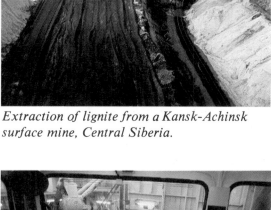

Extraction of lignite from a Kansk-Achinsk surface mine, Central Siberia.

Central control room of exploratory drill ship Viktor Muravlenko.

Construction workers study blueprints for Urengoy gas turbines.

Oil and Gas

The Soviet Union, abundantly endowed with energy resources, is now the world's leading oil and natural gas producer and a substantial net exporter of both fuels. As Soviet planners have become aware of their abundant supplies of these resources over the past three decades, they have relied heavily on them to meet the growth in demand. Oil and gas have fueled national economic growth, and the expansion of key sectors of the economy is tied to their availability. The Soviets' rich resources of oil and gas have allowed Moscow to provide the CEMA countries and other client states with low-cost energy and to export crude oil, natural gas, and petroleum products to the West in exchange for hard currency. Oil and gas have also become essential elements in the USSR's strategic position and a symbol of national pride.

Oil and gas resources are widely scattered throughout the Soviet Union but, by and large, are poorly located with respect to areas of demand. With the exception of the Volga-Urals oil region and the Ukrainian SSR gas region, both now on the decline, the economic and population heartland in the west contains mostly minor oil- and gas-bearing basins. The large sedimentary basins containing the main reserves that will provide the USSR with most of its oil and gas for the rest of this century are in the once virtually unpopulated West Siberia region, where severe environmental conditions, inadequate economic infrastructure, and high development costs will hamper exploitation.

The rapid increase in Soviet oil and gas production is a testament to the size of the reserve base, which by most estimates is among the largest in the world. The Soviets' strong position in oil and gas production should continue into the next century since a number of major potential hydrocarbon-bearing regions remain virtually unexplored and exploration of offshore areas other than the Caspian is just beginning.

Oil Reserves

Since 1947 Moscow has treated the size and location of its oil reserves as a state secret, publishing only occasional, fragmentary, and inconsistent data. Most US and West European oil experts believe that Soviet proved reserves are in the range of 60-80 billion barrels, about 10 to 12 percent of the world's total. Reserves in geologically promising but unexplored areas such as the Barents and Kara Seas and East Siberia could significantly raise the overall amount of proved reserves, putting the USSR in an enviable position compared to other industrialized nations.

Potential oil reserves, however, hold little significance for the Soviet oil supply during the 1980s and into the 1990s. Current production will depend almost entirely on hydrocarbon-bearing structures already discovered whose reserves can be rapidly exploited. As the Soviets have been forced to move their search for new deposits into more remote parts of West Siberia, they have encountered smaller fields, lower production levels, and increased development costs.

Baku, on the shores of the Caspian Sea, was the earliest center of extractive activity, but it declined rapidly after World War II. The Soviets then moved in the 1950s and 1960s to the north and east into their "second Baku," the Volga-Urals basin. The Volga-Urals was the focus of Soviet oil activity for two decades and is still the second-largest producing area. Production from this region is now declining as major fields and reserves are being depleted.

In the early 1960s large new reserves were discovered in the remote and environmentally hostile West Siberian basin, which contains the richest known nydrocarbon deposits in the country. This prolific basin provided most of the growth in oil output during the 1970s and early 1980s and, according to Soviet statements, will remain the leading producing region into the 1990s.

Although West Siberian oil production is expected to increase for several more years, the rate of growth has slowed. Some oil industry officials are now arguing openly that the Soviets must search more aggressively for new reserves in virgin regions of the country such as East Siberia and offshore basins in the Kara and Barents Seas. The Soviets acknowledge, however, that production from these areas will not begin during this decade.

Oil and Gas Regions

Scale 1:39,000,000

0   500 Kilometers

0   500 Statute Miles

Natural Gas Reserves

Unlike the policy for oil reserves, the Soviets do publish information about the size and location of their enormous natural gas reserves. In January 1983 the Soviet Union had explored reserves of about 34 trillion cubic meters, 40 percent of the world's total and enough to sustain rapid growth in production for several decades. Although the rate of discovery of new reserves has slowed considerably since the mid-1970s, total reserves probably will continue to rise for the near term. The location of these reserves, however, has created serious production and transportation problems because most are concentrated in remote Arctic regions. The northern part of Tyumen' Oblast in West Siberia contains about 80 percent of the Soviet gas reserves.

Soviet natural gas production, like that of oil, has increased through the successive development of newly discovered reserves. By the time the North Caucasus region, which was predominant in the early postwar years, reached its peak in the late 1960s, the Ukrainian gasfields had been developed and accounted for most of the growth in production until the early 1970s. Subsequently, gasfields in Central Asia, the Orenburg region of the Volga-Urals, and the Komi ASSR were developed and provided much of the growth during the mid-1970s. Growth in these regions has slowed, and West Siberia is now the primary Soviet gas-producing area. Six northern Tyumen' fields—Urengoy, Yamburg, Zapolyarnoye, Medvezh'ye, Kharasavey, and Bovanenko—together hold more than three-fourths of West Siberia's reserves. Urengoy, with reserves of almost 8 trillion cubic meters, is the world's largest gasfield.

No new, large natural gas region is being developed as a successor to West Siberia, but its enormous reserves are believed to be large enough to support sustained growth into the next century. Long-term future expansion is likely to depend on finding new gas reserves in East Siberia, the Soviet Far East, and offshore areas such as the Barents and Kara Seas.

Gas Condensate

In addition to crude oil and gas, the Soviet Union possesses large reserves of condensate—the liquid hydrocarbons that condense from associated and nonassociated gas when it is extracted from the reservoir—which are included in oil production statistics. Out of a total oil output of 12.33 million barrels per day (b/d) in 1983, about 600,000 b/d are believed to be gas condensate. Although Moscow has never published official reserve totals for gas condensate, limited data from the gas ministry suggest that the condensate reserve base is more than large enough to support current and future output requirements well into the next century.

Reserves of gas condensate are widely distributed in many parts of the USSR, with numerous deposits in West Siberia, Komi ASSR, Central Asia, and the Ukraine. West Siberia may contain as much as two-thirds of all USSR condensate resources, primarily at Urengoy and the large oilfields of the middle Ob' region. The remaining portion of the known condensate reserve base is located at a relatively small number of large fields such as Orenburg in the southern Urals, Vuktyl in the Komi ASSR, and the high-sulfur gasfields of Central Asia.

Night drilling in the Komi ASSR.

Reserves in geologically promising but unexplored areas such as the Barents and Kara Seas and East Siberia could significantly raise proved reserves.

The West Siberian Oil and Gas Region

Although it possesses one of the Earth's most forbidding and difficult environments, West Siberia produces 60 percent of the nation's oil and roughly 50 percent of its natural gas, having surpassed the declining Volga-Urals region in oil output in 1978 and Soviet Central Asia in gas production in 1979. To meet Soviet domestic and export needs for these fuels by 1985, the region, according to the current five-year plan (1981-85), will have to produce 63 percent of the nation's oil (8 million b/d are planned) and increase its share of natural gas production to 57 percent (357 billion cubic meters). As production moves farther north in West Siberia, the average cost per unit of output will rise because of higher operating and investment outlays required for exploration, extraction, and transportation.

The oil and gas region is in the West Siberian lowland, one of the world's largest and flattest plains, and, consequently, one of the most poorly drained and flood prone. More than half of the land area of West Siberia is swamp or marshland. In the spring, flood waters of the Ob' and Irtysh Rivers, flowing from the south, are jammed by ice that has not yet melted in the north, and broad areas are inundated.

In addition, severe winter temperatures and cold winds make the West Siberian oil and gas region one of the harshest environments in which to work in the world. Before the discovery of oil and gas in 1960, the entire area was uninhabited wilderness except for hunters and trappers. All endeavors entail a struggle against the environment and result in sharply increased costs to exploit West Siberia's valuable hydrocarbon resources.

All seasons in some way seriously impair the effectiveness of men and machines in northern Siberia. The severe cold in winter as well as the swampy conditions in summer reduce the service life of vehicles and machinery. Average winter temperatures of −20°C and below substantially reduce workers' productivity; Soviet work regulations prohibit outdoor work when temperatures reach −40°C and wind speeds exceed 15 meters per second. This produces a windchill effect comparable to −110°F and causes bare skin to freeze in less than 30 seconds. Moreover, swarms of flies and mosquitoes, which saturate the region during the warm season, take an additional toll on worker efficiency and health.

Geologic Setting

Occupying an area of more than 3 million square kilometers, the West Siberian basin is the largest structural-sedimentary basin in the world. Favorable geologic conditions have also made it, in the estimation of most petroleum geologists, one of the better locations in the world for the accumulation of hydrocarbon deposits.

Geologically, the basin deepens to the north, where the sediments generally range up to 6 to 8 kilometers in thickness. In the southern and central parts of the basin, the sediments are 3 to 5 kilometers thick. The sedimentary cover of the basin consists of marine and continental deposits of the Jurassic, Cretaceous, and Paleocene ages, overlain by more recent glacial, lake, and stream deposits.

Surface elevations seldom exceed 100 meters above sea level except on an east-west line of low glacial hills that divides the region into two parts. To the south of this divide, where the main oil deposits have been found, rivers flow southward to the middle Ob' River; to the north, where the region's natural gas is found, they flow northward to the lower Ob' and the Arctic Ocean.

Development

Following the initial discovery of gas at Berezovo in the mid-1950s and oil at Shaim in 1960, the search for hydrocarbons shifted to the mid-

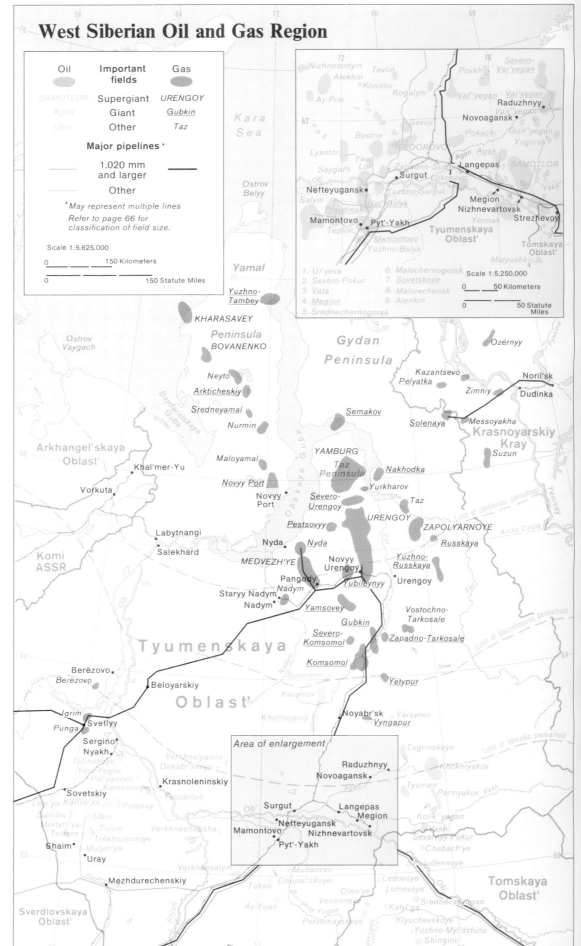

dle Ob' region. Here, during the 1960s, the Soviets discovered and began developing a number of oilfields with relatively high-quality reservoirs.

The immense Samotlor oilfield was discovered in the middle Ob' region of Tyumen' Oblast in 1965 and put into production in 1969. The supergiant Samotlor field near Nizhnevartovsk was soon recognized as one of the largest oilfields in the world. During the 1970s Samotlor

Key Settlements

Most key West Siberian settlements developed along major waterways as ports and supply bases for the region's early exploration and development. Many became major supply and housing centers on the road and rail systems that later penetrated the region. They now serve as the focuses of the region's expanding pipeline and petroleum processing facilities.

Labytnangi (66°39'N/66°21'E) Population: est. 11,000. From this railhead on the lower Ob', cargo is transferred to rivercraft bound for gas exploitation areas.

Mamontovo/Pyt'-Yakh (60°46'N/72°47'E, 60°45'N/72°50'E) Population: est. 10,000. Housing and storage areas at Mamontovo settlement and the adjacent Pyt'-Yakh rail station support Mamontovo oilfield.

Megion (61°03'N/76°06'E) Population: est. over 10,000. Megion provides housing and logistic support for surrounding oilfields. All-weather roads lead to these fields and to Nizhnevartovsk.

Nadym (65°32'N/72°32'E) Population: est. 50,000. One of the largest urban centers in the northern gas development area has schools, stores, and community services for workers of the surrounding gas region. Its population is expected to increase to about 150,000.

Nefteyugansk (61°56'N/76°38'E) Population: est. 72,000 (1984). This is the primary port and supply base for the Mamontovo and Ust-Balyk oilfields. It is linked to them by all-weather roads.

Nizhnevartovsk (60°56'N/76°38'E) Population: est. 178,000 (1984). Nizhnevartovsk supports the Samotlor oilfield and smaller fields nearby. It has extensive port facilities on the Ob' River, a rail tie with Surgut, all-weather roads, and an airport.

Novoagansk (61°57'N/76°41'E) Population: est. 7,000. Located at the western edge of the Var'yegan oil-producing area, Novoagansk is a support base for oil exploitation and transport.

Novyy Urengoy (66°06'N/76°35'E) Population: est. 52,000 (1984). Novyy Urengoy, served by rail and air, is the main support city for the Urengoy natural gasfield. Industries and high-rise apartments are under construction.

Noyabr'sk (63°08'N/75°22'E) Population: est. 55,000 (1984). Noyabr'sk, a new urban center for the Kholmogory oilfield and other oil and gas exploitation, has a rail-served storage area covering 3.5 square kilometers.

Pangody (65°51'N/74°30'E) Population: est. 6,000. Pangody is the supply base of the Medvezh'ye gasfield.

Raduzhnyy (62°06'N/77°31'E) Population: est. 5,000. Raduzhnyy supports nearby oilfields and is the terminus of an all-weather road from Nizhnevartovsk, 140 km to the south.

Sergino (62°30'N/65°38'E) Population: est. 6,000. Sergino is a rail terminus where cargo is transferred to rivercraft or to trucks plying the winter road to the Urengoy gasfield.

Staryy Nadym (65°35'N/72°42'E) Population: est. 2,000. This expanding port serves the city of Nadym (11 km southwest) and the Medvezh'ye and Urengoy gasfields.

Strezhevoy (60°42'N/77°34'E) Population: est. 10,000. This port, 60 km southeast of Nizhnevartovsk supports the Sovetskoye oilfield and may support new oil exploration along the Vakh River.

Surgut (61°14'N/73°20'E) Population: est. 188,000 (1984). Surgut is the key housing, industrial, and supply center of the middle Ob' oil region; it has large mechanized port facilities, an all-weather airport, and rail facilities.

Uray (60°08'N/64°48'E) Population: est. 20,000. Uray, which supports an oil exploitation area west of the Ob', is served by rivercraft and an all-weather airport; a dirt road connects to a railhead at Mezhdurechenskiy.

Urengoy (65°58'N/78°25'E) Population: est. 9,000. Development of Urengoy gasfields stimulated construction of port facilities and storage areas. These facilities are expanding along the left bank to the site of the railyard and projected city of Tikhiy.

surpassed Romashkino to become the Soviet's premier oilfield and was singularly responsible for the rapid growth in Soviet oil output during that decade. By 1980 Samotlor was yielding about 25 percent of total Soviet oil production and accounted for about 50 percent of West Siberian oil output. Production at Fedorovo, West Siberia's second-largest oilfield, started in 1973 and began to grow rapidly following the intensification of drilling in the late 1970s as output from Samotlor was beginning to level off. In 1982 Fedorovo accounted for approximately 6 percent of Soviet national output.

Explored natural gas deposits in West Siberia are concentrated in the Arctic regions of the Tyumen' Oblast. Production from Medvezh'ye, which began in 1972, and from Urengoy, which began in 1978, is to be followed by Yamburg and ultimately extend to other supergiants—Zapolyarnoye, Kharasavey, and Bovanenko.

Permafrost

North of 64 degrees N latitude, West Siberian oil and gas exploration and extraction are affected by frozen ground or permafrost—a phenomenon that occurs where mean annual temperatures are below freezing. Permafrost complicates all oil and gas activity and seismic exploration; special drilling muds and concretes are necessary to avoid alternate freezing and thawing problems, and well casing has to be carefully insulated to prevent collapse. Maintenance of facilities is often more expensive than their initial construction since seasonal freezing and thawing cause the ground to heave, cracking foundations and collapsing structures.

In the northernmost areas, permafrost is generally continuous and lies within 1 or 2 meters of the surface, creating surface drainage problems. Only a shallow layer of soil thaws each summer. Southward, the surface layer that freezes and thaws seasonally becomes deeper and the underlying permafrost becomes discontinuous. At its southernmost limits, permafrost is reduced to sporadic patches, as in the Surgut and Nizhnevartovsk areas.

Population and Settlement

Population growth—particularly urban—has been dramatic during the two decades since oil and gas exploitation began in West Siberia. In the two administrative subunits of Tyumen' Oblast where energy development is now concentrated, the population increased from 186,000 in 1959 to 1.2 million in 1983, or from one-tenth to one-fourth of West Siberia's total. Whereas urban residents comprised less than half of the population in 1959, in 1984 four-fifths of the total lived in 44 urban settlements. Of the 44 urban places, 38 were founded after 1960 and 26 of these are oil and gas related; the largest are Surgut and Nizhnevartovsk.

The rapid and large population influx into West Siberia has required the construction of a network of settlements—with attendant housing, stores, schools, clinics, utilities, and related industrial installations. Lack of comfortable housing and amenities is the primary reason that four-fifths of the 500,000 migrants who arrive yearly soon leave the region.

Population Trends in Tyumenskaya Oblast'

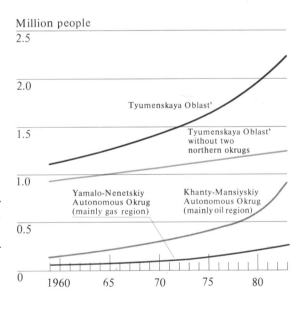

Million people

Tyumenskaya Oblast'

Tyumenskaya Oblast' without two northern okrugs

Yamalo-Nenetskiy Autonomous Okrug (mainly gas region)

Khanty-Mansiyskiy Autonomous Okrug (mainly oil region)

Variations of Permafrost

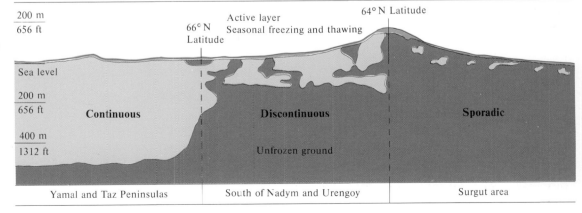

200 m / 656 ft

Active layer — Seasonal freezing and thawing

64° N Latitude

66° N Latitude

Sea level

200 m / 656 ft

Continuous

Discontinuous

Sporadic

400 m / 1312 ft

Unfrozen ground

Yamal and Taz Peninsulas

South of Nadym and Urengoy

Surgut area

17

Administration of West Siberian Development

The buildup of the region has involved the efforts of 26 ministries and state agencies pursuing their own plans. Concerned about the poorly coordinated management of the region, Moscow in 1981 established the unique, interdepartmental Territorial Commission for the Development of the West Siberian Oil and Gas Complex. Headquartered in Tyumen', this group includes 31 major directors and heads of organizations responsible for development in West Siberia. Representatives from the State Planning Committee (Gosplan) and the Central Committee of the Communist Party of the USSR also participate. The commission has no authority of its own and must submit its proposals and recommendations for regional development directly to Gosplan.

Transportation Systems

The construction and maintenance of a reliable transportation network are essential in developing West Siberian resources, which are located thousands of kilometers from material suppliers and markets. Nearly all construction material,

equipment, and consumer goods are imported into the West Siberian oil and gas region, and transport systems are severely strained.

The Trans-Siberian Railroad crosses the West Siberian plain a few hundred kilometers south of the oil and gas region. In addition, only one trunk railroad extends into the main oil and gas region—a single-track, diesel-traction line from the Urals, via Tyumen', to Surgut, Nizhnevartovsk, and, in 1983, northward to Novyy Urengoy. The oilfields west of the Ob' are served by a rail line from the Urals. Another line brings freight to Sergino for transfer to ships and barges on the Ob' or, in winter, to trucks for long hauls via winter roads to the northern gasfields. A rail line to Labytnangi on the Ob' also brings freight to be transferred to the river fleet. A temporary gasfield rail line shuttling freight from the river port at Staryy Nadym to the Medvezh'ye and Urengoy gasfields is now being converted to a regular railroad extending the line that reached Novyy Urengoy in 1983.

After 20 years of building, the region's road network is still poorly developed, and the demand for roads grows faster than they are built. The situation is similar to the one faced by the United States in exploiting Alaska's energy

resources. There are few all-weather (paved or gravel) roads, and most others are often impassable between May and September. In winter, however, cross-country travel is accomplished on ice roads built by spreading water over the ground or on snow roads built by compacting snow.

Without passable roads through the swamps, many supply and construction activities must wait until winter. Winter roads are vital to early exploitation of new fields and for pipeline construction and maintenance. An impressive example that serves both these purposes is a 700-kilometer winter road linking the Sergino rail terminus to Novyy Urengoy.

Despite the short navigation season caused by long and severe winters, waterways play a key role as links between railroads and the roads serving the fields. Most river freight to the oil and gas region is routed downstream (north) from rail/river junctions at Omsk, Novosibirsk, Tobol'sk, and Tyumen' to the sub-Arctic ports such as Surgut and Nizhnevartovsk on the middle Ob'.

The navigation season ranges from five months (late May to late October) at Surgut to less than

Air transport, particularily by helicopters, is commonly used to augment road, rail, and water transport in West Siberia.

one month at the extreme northern port of Nyda. During this season, much of the freight is transferred to small ships and barges for transport up small rivers, such as the Agan in the middle Ob' region and the Nadym and Pur farther north.

While air transport provides only a small percentage of the cargo moved into the region, it is particularly important because it can be used when other modes of transportation are unavailable. Year-round air links have been established between major Soviet cities, such as Moscow and Chelyabinsk, and the larger cities of the region—Surgut, Nefteyugansk, Nizhnevartovsk, Strezhevoy, Novyy Urengoy, and Nadym.

Helicopter pads are located at almost every settlement and drilling area. Helicopters are used in laying pipe, building compressor stations, hauling supplies, delivering field crews, and constructing powerlines.

During summer, river barges are frequently used to transport rigs to new drilling sites.

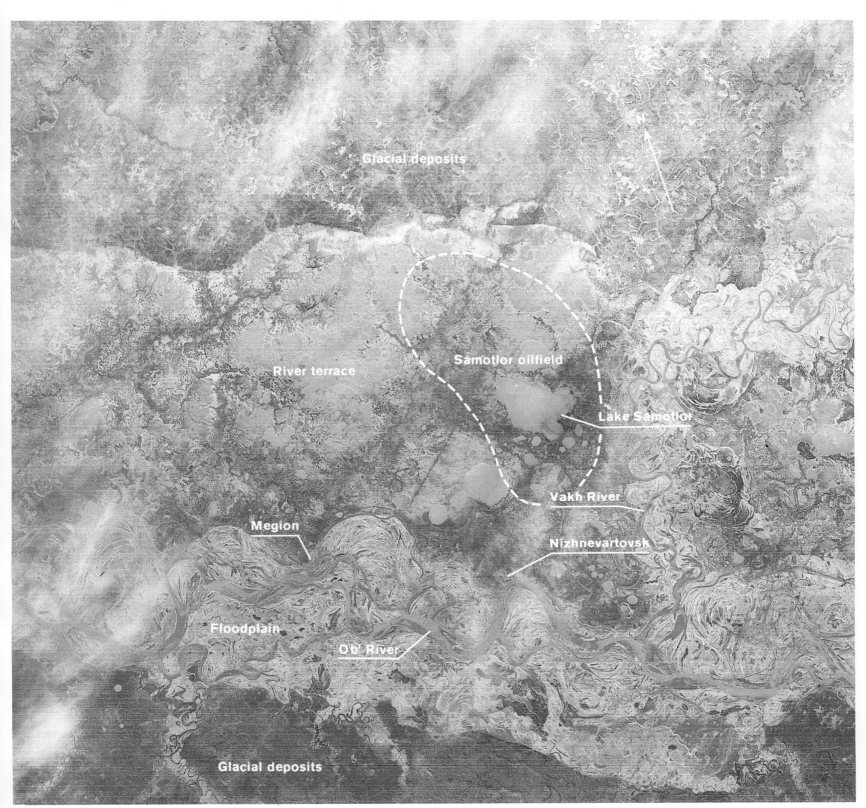

Samotlor oilfield and nearby Ob' River as seen from Landsat.

Other Major Oil and Gas Regions

Volga-Urals

The Volga-Urals oil-producing region covers about 500,000 square kilometers between the Volga River and the Ural Mountains. It produces 25 percent of the USSR's oil—second only to West Siberia. The region includes the Tatar, Bashkir, and Udmurt Republics and the Kuybyshev and Perm' Oblasts. Other oblasts usually associated with the region are Orenburg, Saratov, and Volgograd.

Production in the "second Baku" began in the 1930s, but growth in oil output did not start to accelerate until the 1950s, when the supergiant Romashkino and Arlan fields and several other major deposits were developed. The Volga-Urals was the leading oil-producing region from the 1950s until it was surpassed by West Siberia in 1978.

Output from all major producing areas of the Volga-Urals has been declining since it peaked at 4.5 million b/d in 1975. Many fields have been producing for 20 to 30 years and their easily obtainable reserves are nearly depleted. Production wells are lifting increasing amounts of water with the remaining oil. Even with deeper drilling efforts and expanded use of secondary and enhanced oil recovery techniques, the region's share of national output has been steadily declining. It is doubtful that production from newer fields in the Udmurt ASSR and elsewhere in the region will be sufficient to slow the overall decline of the Volga-Urals.

Significant gas production in the Volga-Urals began with the development of the giant Orenburg field, southwest of the Ural Mountains, in the late 1960s. Most of Orenburg's gas has been exported since the CEMA nations completed the Orenburg or Soyuz pipeline to Eastern Europe in 1978. An additional large gas deposit is being developed at Karachaganak, south of Orenburg in Kazakhstan.

Timan-Pechora (Komi ASSR)

The Timan-Pechora basin is a sedimentary basin of 350,000 square kilometers in the northeastern part of the European USSR. It is part of two administrative subdivisions: the Komi ASSR and the Nenets Autonomous Okrug. Development of the petroleum basin occurred in two phases. The first phase was from the early 1930s to the 1950s when the area south of the Pechora and Usa Rivers was explored and small oil and gas fields were put into production. The second phase began in the early 1960s with the exploration of Arctic areas nearer the Barents Sea. Two fields—Usinsk which was discovered in 1963, and Vozey, in 1972—accounted for more than 60 percent of Komi oil production in 1982.

Komi ASSR, one of the two oil regions outside West Siberia, has shown no significant growth in oil production since 1979. Although the region appears to have substantial oil resources,

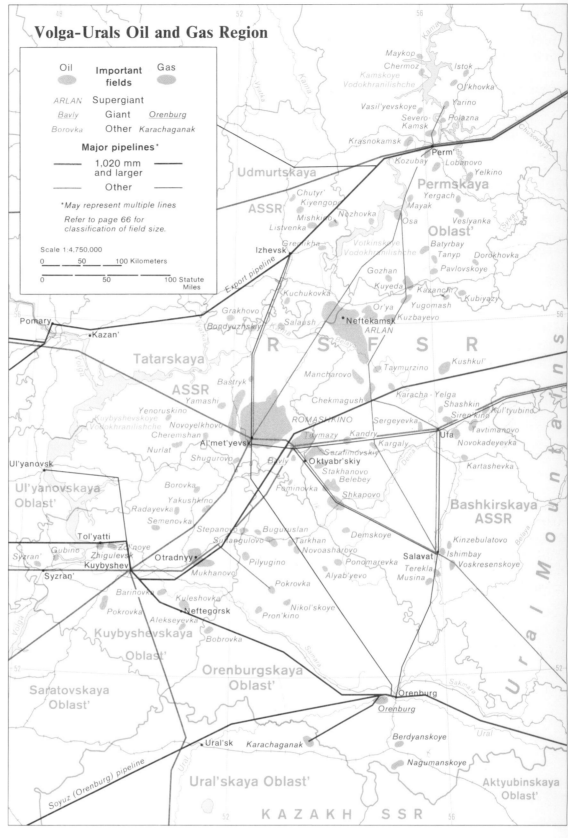

Volga-Urals Oil and Gas Region

development has been slowed by the extreme Arctic environment and by the heavy and paraffinic oils that are characteristic of the region. Nevertheless, the Soviets hope to increase oil output from the region again.

Komi ASSR gas production was insignificant until the giant Vuktyl gas deposit was developed in the late 1960s. While there are more than 30 gasfields in Komi ASSR, none of the others approaches the size of Vuktyl, which in 1982 accounted for nearly all of Komi ASSR's approximately 18-billion-cubic-meter production. Vuktyl gas production was responsible for the construction of the Northern Lights pipeline from Komi ASSR to Eastern Europe.

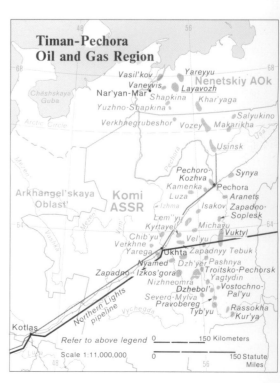

Timan-Pechora Oil and Gas Region

North Caucasus–North Caspian

The North Caucasus–North Caspian oil and gas region follows a productive geologic trend more than 1,500 km from the Ukraine eastward across the Caspian Sea into Kazakhstan.

The North Caucasus region, situated west of the Caspian Sea, has been a petroleum producer for more than 60 years. In the late 1950s, as output from early producing wells began to decline, many deeper wells were drilled to increase production. Output in the North Caucasus peaked at about 740,000 b/d in 1971 and then declined to 400,000 b/d in 1980 as production fell rapidly in the most productive area, the Chechen-Ingush ASSR. Oil production in the region's other areas—Stavropol' Kray, Krasnodar Kray, and the Dagestan ASSR—is also declining.

East of the Caspian, Kazakhstan's oil development is primarily located in three areas: the Mangyshlak Peninsula, dominated by the giant Uzen' field; the Buzachi Peninsula, with several deposits of heavy oil; and the Emba region, the source of early Kazakhstan production.

Natural gas production in the North Caucasus–North Caspian has been declining since the late 1960s. A recently discovered field north of Astrakhan' on the lower Volga, however, may prove to be as large as the giant Orenburg field. Astrakhan' gas is high in sulfur and carbon dioxide (sour gas), and the USSR is acquiring Western technology and corrosion-resistant equipment to develop the field and remove the impurities from the gas.

Caspian Sea oil workers.

Transcaucasus–Central Asia

The Transcaucasus–Central Asia oil and gas regions extend from the Georgian and Azerbaijan SSRs in the Caucasus Mountains under the southern Caspian Sea across Central Asia's Turkmen and Uzbek SSRs.

Oilfields near Baku, in Azerbaijan, began producing in the 19th century. They accounted for half of the world's oil production in 1900 and more than 70 percent of Soviet oil output in 1941. Azerbaijan's oil industry declined during World War II and, although it never regained prewar production levels, again rose until 1966, accounting for 8 percent of total Soviet production. Postwar growth was spurred mainly by

offshore wells in the Caspian Sea, which now account for more than 70 percent of Azerbaijan's output. Transcaucasus oil development extends from Baku westward into the Georgian SSR, where oil production, though relatively small, is rising. Georgia's output—about 60,000 b/d in 1980—is primarily from the Samgori field near Tbilisi.

Central Asia played a crucial role in Soviet natural gas production during the late 1960s and early 1970s by offsetting declining growth in the European USSR during West Siberia's early development. From 1973, when output surpassed that of the Ukraine, to 1979, when output was in turn surpassed by that of West Siberia, Central Asia was the leading gas-producing region in the USSR. During this period it accounted for more than 30 percent of total USSR production. Turkmenistan has recently replaced Uzbekistan as the major gas-producing area in Central Asia. Despite outputs from West Siberia's supergiant gasfields, surplus gas from both sparsely populated Central Asian republics continues to be integrated into the vast Soviet domestic and export pipeline network.

Future petroleum growth in the Transcaucasus and Central Asia regions will probably come from deeper drilling in the Caspian Sea rather than from the current oil and gas exploration efforts in western Azerbaijan and Turkmenistan. Any new discoveries would require nearly a decade before they would make a significant contribution to Soviet oil production.

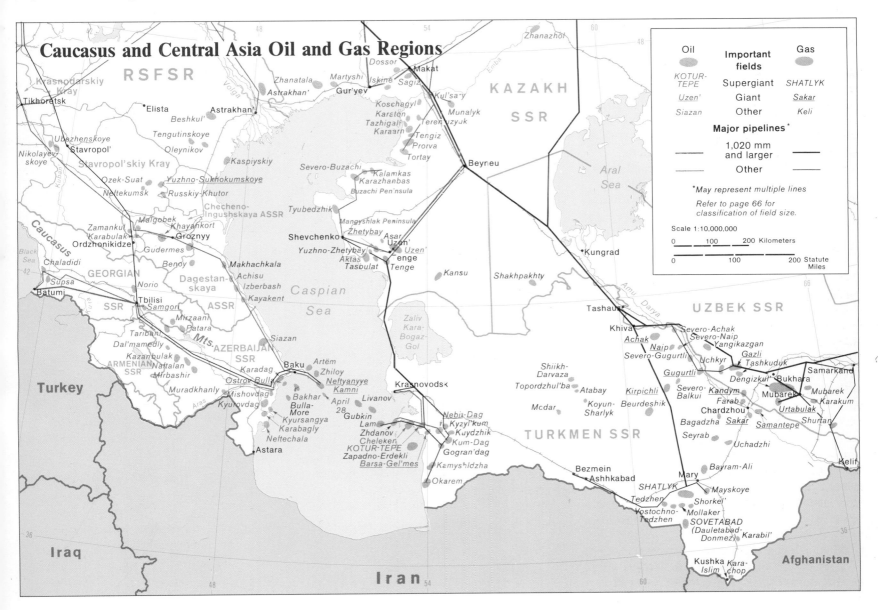

Caucasus and Central Asia Oil and Gas Regions

Production and Consumption

Oil

For 30 years after World War II, oil production in the Soviet Union grew at enviable rates. During the mid-1970s the USSR became the world's leading oil producer. In 1983 the Soviet oil industry reported an average daily production rate of 12.33 million barrels of crude oil and gas condensate, about 20 percent more than the United States.

The rapid growth in production was largely the result of the discovery and exploration of a series of large, giant, and supergiant fields. In the 1950s and 1960s, the Soviets developed the Volga-Urals and the massive fields of Romashkino and Arlan. By the 1970s, just as production growth from the western USSR was beginning to taper off, the Soviets received a boost in production from the mammoth fields of the West Siberian basin—Samotlor, Fedorovo, and Mamontovo.

Soviet oil growth has begun to slow. The Soviets failed to make either the original or revised production targets for 1980 and have not equaled or exceeded an original annual target since the early 1970s. Plans have been revised downward to the point where the 1985 plan goal of 12.6 million b/d is no higher than the original target—later revised downward—for 1980. The present 1985 goal, already lowered from the upper limit of 12.9 million b/d, a provisional output goal, represents planned growth of less than 1 percent per year.

These small increases have been possible only because the Soviets have been able to keep West Siberian production growing—from 6.2 million b/d in 1980 to an estimated 7.4 million b/d in 1983. West Siberia's share of national output is now 60 percent. Outside West Siberia, only two lesser oil-producing regions of the USSR are currently able to raise output—the Komi ASSR, in the north European USSR, and Kazakhstan, on the eastern shore of the Caspian Sea. These three growth areas, together with the declining Volga-Urals region, produce more than 90 percent of Soviet oil and will largely determine Soviet output in the 1980s.

Oil production in all other major Soviet producing regions has leveled off or is declining. Volga-Urals production has declined by 1.2 million b/d—or 25 percent—since its peak in 1975. The drop was largely the result of a decline at the supergiant Romashkino oilfield, the leading producer in the region and the second-largest field in the USSR.

The USSR's first-place position in world oil production is primarily the result of its abundant resource base, massive investment, and sheer persistence rather than of any unique technical and managerial effort on the part of its oil industry. Although accorded high-priority status in the civilian economy, the oil industry is troubled by many of the same problems that afflict other Soviet industries—equipment shortages, technology shortcomings, and lagging productivity and efficiency. Moscow has been at-

tempting to rectify this with substantial foreign equipment purchases and domestic technology enhancements.

Some 70 percent of oil consumption in the Soviet Union takes place in three sectors of the economy: electric power, transportation, and industry. Although Soviet oil consumption during the last 25 years has consistently grown faster than total energy consumption, in recent years the rates of both have been declining as overall economic growth has decreased. In the first half of the 1970s, oil consumption grew about 7 percent annually (compared with 4.7 percent for total energy), but during the period 1976-80 growth in oil use fell to 4 percent per year (versus 3.5 percent for total energy). Soviet efforts over the last five to 10 years to slow the growth of domestic oil consumption, except in the industrial sector, have been minimal. Domestic oil consumption in 1983 is estimated at 9.0 million b/d.

USSR: Oil Production[a] and Apparent Consumption

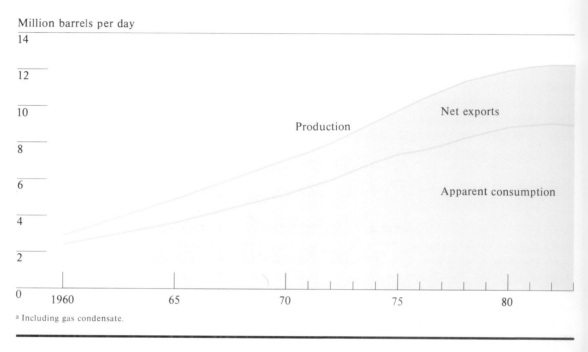

Million barrels per day

Production

Net exports

Apparent consumption

[a] Including gas condensate.

USSR: Oil Production by Region[a]

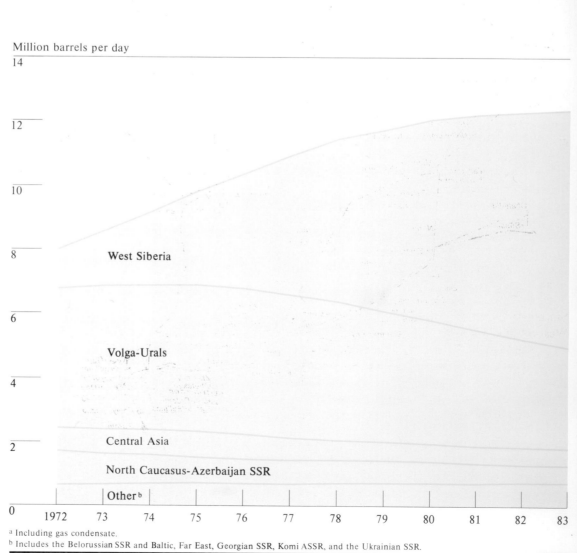

Million barrels per day

West Siberia

Volga-Urals

Central Asia

North Caucasus-Azerbaijan SSR

Other[b]

[a] Including gas condensate.
[b] Includes the Belorussian SSR and Baltic, Far East, Georgian SSR, Komi ASSR, and the Ukrainian SSR.

Natural Gas

Natural gas, rather than oil, has paced the growth in Soviet energy production in recent years. Not only is Moscow turning to gas to satisfy a large part of its increasing internal demand for energy in the 1980s, it is also relying on gas as an important source of hard currency revenue.

In 1983 the USSR surpassed the United States as the world's largest producer of natural gas. Soviet gas output of 536 billion cubic meters in 1983 compared with 450 billion cubic meters for the United States. Even if the Soviets fall short of their 630-billion-cubic-meter gas production goal for 1985, they are expected to remain in first place.

The European USSR—primarily the North Caucasus and the Ukraine—supplied 85 percent of natural gas produced in 1965. Following the discovery of the Orenburg field in the late 1960s, the Volga-Urals and Central Asia fields paced Soviet production growth during the 1970s. By 1983 West Siberia was providing nearly all of the gas industry's growth and accounted for one-half of the nation's gas production.

The first gasfields to be developed in West Siberia were located along the lower Ob' River, near Berezovo, where production began in 1966. The center of the West Siberian deposits, however, is located much farther to the north and east near the Arctic Circle. Of the six large fields there—Medvezh'ye, Urengoy, Yamburg, Zapolyarnoye, Kharasavey, and Bovanenko—only Medvezh'ye and Urengoy have been developed. The opening of Medvezh'ye in 1972 marked the beginning of West Siberia's rapid growth in gas production, and by 1978 it supplied about three-fourths of the region's total output.

West Siberia's Urengoy gasfield, brought into production in 1978 along with the smaller Vyngapur field, is currently being intensively developed and will account for virtually all the growth in Soviet gas production during the next several years. In 1982 Urengoy's production of 117 billion cubic meters was less than one-half the field's planned annual production for the mid-1980s. The supergiant Urengoy field, with reserves of 7.8 trillion cubic meters, is the largest gasfield in the world. Additionally, the Soviets are making preparations to start developing the adjacent Yamburg gasfield to the north in the late 1980s.

Since natural gas production increments in West Siberia exceed declines in the older regions, the total USSR output continues to increase. Furthermore, West Siberia has become a principal supplier of natural gas to Europe through several long pipeline systems that extend as far as France.

Currently, natural gas provides four-fifths as much domestic energy as oil, compared with only 63 percent in 1970. Gas output has grown an average of 8 percent per year since 1970. The Soviets plan to raise the share of natural gas in total primary energy production from 26 percent in 1980 to 32 percent in 1985.

USSR: Natural Gas Production

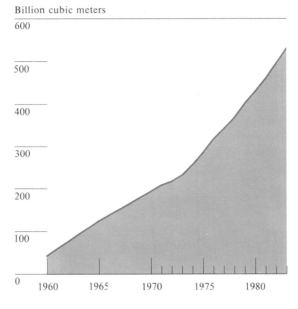

Billion cubic meters

Gas Condensate

Gas condensate, also called natural gas liquids, is a hydrocarbon occurring either in natural gas or oil reservoirs. Condensate is normally in the vapor phase at reservoir temperatures and pressures, but condenses either at lower reservoir pressures or at the surface during extraction. Condensate can be processed to yield fractions usable as petrochemical feedstock, motor gasoline, "bottled gas," and raw materials for other industrial uses.

Significant production of condensate was not achieved until the early 1970s, when the Soviets first began to add condensate totals to their crude oil production output. By 1975 production had risen to 250,000 b/d with some 155,000 b/d coming from two condensate fields—Vuktyl in Komi ASSR and Orenburg in the southern Urals. Since that time national and regional condensate production figures have not been published by the Soviets. But 1983 output is estimated at 600,000 b/d out of 12.33 million b/d of combined crude oil and gas condensate.

Growth has been steady, but the Soviets have encountered numerous problems in expanding condensate output. Condensate development has long taken a backseat in investment allocations, with the oil and gas ministries preferring to concentrate instead on easier and more rewarding oil and natural gas production. Consequently, a large percentage of both oil-associated condensate and condensate available from gas production has been lost because of inadequate processing capacity and inefficient field recovery techniques. Until very recently the Soviets have lagged badly in developing their gas-processing facilities and increasing their condensate recovery totals.

The USSR is now attempting to upgrade the capabilities of its condensate industry and has set ambitious production goals for the 1980s. Substantial production increases from West Siberia, Central Asia, western Kazakhstan, and possibly Komi ASSR can be expected. The Soviets hope to recover about 100,000 b/d from the Urengoy field alone by 1985 and to transport it by a major condensate pipeline to Surgut which, according to some reports, will extend westward to the Volga-Urals. Two other major gas condensate fields, Astrakhan' on the Volga River and Karachaganak in northwestern Kazakhstan, are slated to provide together some 80,000 to 100,000 b/d of condensate by 1985.

USSR: Natural Gas Production by Region

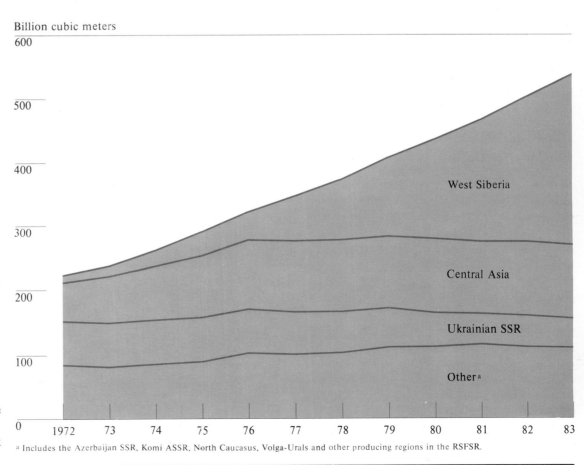

Billion cubic meters

a Includes the Azerbaijan SSR, Komi ASSR, North Caucasus, Volga-Urals and other producing regions in the RSFSR.

Exploration

Exploration and discovery of new hydrocarbon reserves—oil, gas, and gas condensate—are a slow but critical process that will largely determine the Soviets' ability to meet future oil and gas production goals. Soviet energy planners are actively developing a wide range of plans to locate and evaluate both onshore and offshore petroleum reserves. In addition, they are upgrading their exploration capabilities through purchases of equipment from the West, reproduction of Western designs, and strengthening domestic manufacturing capability.

Historically, Soviet exploration philosophy has been to concentrate on one hydrocarbon-bearing province at a time. The bulk of Soviet exploration is currently being conducted in West Siberia in the vicinity of the oil-producing areas of the middle Ob' and the large gasfields in northern Tyumen' Oblast. Exploration there will, by necessity, be moving farther from the developed infrastructure into the more remote regions of the Tyumen' and Tomsk Oblasts.

At the same time, the Soviets have begun limited surveys of the country's remaining 20 unexplored basins for a successor to West Siberia—the third "Baku." Onshore, East Siberia and western Kazakhstan are scheduled for comprehensive regional investigation. Offshore, exploratory drilling has been under way since 1977 in waters near Sakhalin in a cooperative venture with a Japanese consortium. Soviet exploration in the Barents Sea is beginning despite the lack of engineering and technical experience in the Arctic offshore environment. Limited exploration has also started in the Baltic and Black Seas and the Sea of Azov.

Almost all of these basins, both onshore and offshore, are located away from economic and population centers. Some Soviet oil experts have been suggesting that, instead of exploring these remote areas, the search for new oil should be concentrated in the deeper zones of the older Volga-Urals, the North Caspian basin, and the developed areas of the West Siberian basin. Any major program to explore these deeper and more difficult targets would require a significant upgrading of Soviet drilling equipment and technology.

Exploration planning for new hydrocarbon reserves in the Soviet Union is the joint responsibility of the Ministry of Geology, the Ministry of the Petroleum Industry, and the Ministry of the Gas Industry. The Ministries of Geology and Petroleum Industry are tasked with onshore oil exploration; the gas ministry is responsible for all gas exploration as well as offshore oil exploration.

Plans for petroleum exploration are drawn up by these ministries with the assistance of the Academy of Sciences. The various plans are submitted to the State Planning Committee (Gosplan) for approval, after which they are announced at the beginning of each five-year plan period. During the current plan (1981-85) Soviet oilmen were expected to discover and delineate oil and gas reserves that will be translated into production during the late 1980s and 1990s.

Technology and Equipment

Soviet geologists, faced with searching millions of square kilometers of unexplored territory, are using every available technique to locate new hydrocarbon reserves and to decrease the time lag between discovery and the onset of production. Foremost among these is the use of space technology to minimize mapping and select areas for detailed exploration. Research for this effort was centralized in 1978 in Aerogeologiya, a geologic institute which applies space photography to terrain analysis to pinpoint promising areas for seismic surveys.

The Soviets employ standard reflection and refraction seismic techniques in exploration but

Exploration for oil and gas in the Soviet Arctic.

are hampered by technology shortcomings. Refraction studies can locate large amplitude structures—like Romashkino or Samotlor—but lack the higher resolution to identify smaller deposits. Seismic equipment in the USSR is rated to depths of about 3,000 meters, and there is little chance that this equipment will be able to detect deeper deposits or the more subtle stratigraphic traps.

The Soviets made significant strides in offshore exploration technology during the 1970s, but they fell far short of their original goals. They had intended to have 10 mobile jack-up drilling platforms in operation in the Caspian and Black Seas by 1980, but only four were operating in that year. Efforts to obtain Western offshore

Seismic Exploration

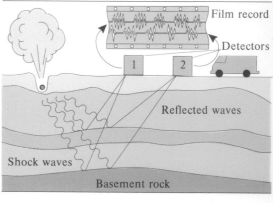

Fixed drilling platform in the "April 28" oilfield, Caspian Sea.

"Baky" mobile jack-up drilling platform in the Caspian Sea.

Areas of Current Oil and Gas Exploration

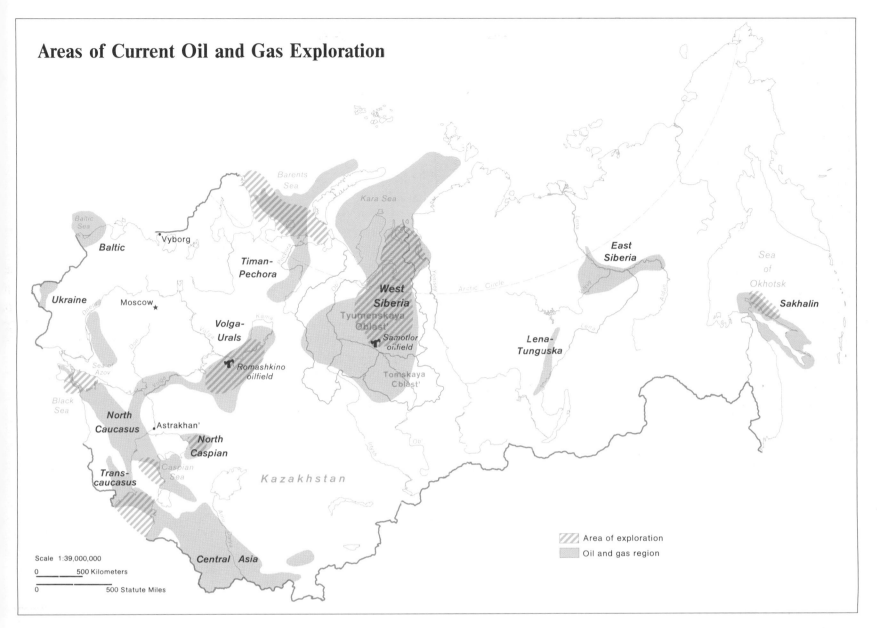

Scale 1:39,000,000

0 —— 500 Kilometers

0 —— 500 Statute Miles

Area of exploration
Oil and gas region

"Shelf 2" semisubmersible drilling platform in the Bay of Baku.

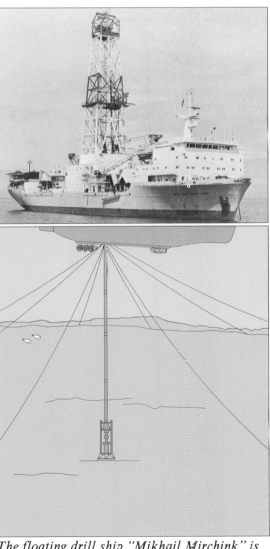

The floating drill ship "Mikhail Mirchink" is one of three built by Finland for the Soviets.

equipment and technology were delayed by prolonged discussions and negotiations which postponed actual deliveries.

The USSR plans to concentrate offshore exploratory drilling for the next few years in the Caspian Sea, the Sea of Okhotsk near Sakhalin, and the Barents and Baltic Seas. Fabrication yards at Astrakhan' on the Caspian and Vyborg on the Gulf of Finland are now producing mobile offshore drilling platforms. The first Soviet-built, semisubmersible platform—Shelf 1—began Caspian operations in early 1982. A second semisubmersible platform—Shelf 2—was completed in 1982. As of mid-1984 the USSR had 11 mobile offshore drilling platforms in operation—eight jack-ups and three semisubmersibles. Three semisubmersible and one jack-up drilling rig are being constructed at Astrakhan' and Vyborg. To begin exploration of the Arctic offshore region, the Soviets have bought three drill ships from Finland.

Drilling

The past three decades have seen a fourfold increase in Soviet oil and gas drilling in terms of meters drilled. In an effort to maximize output between 1965 and 1980, the Soviets emphasized development drilling rather than exploration drilling. Plans now call for even more rapid growth in development drilling and a substantial increase in exploration drilling.

In the USSR, development drilling within oil and gas fields follows specific phases. After a discovery, several confirmation wells are drilled to learn more about the dimensions and geologic parameters of the new field and to obtain early well production data. Based on the results from early production, as well as on information from exploration wells, a field development plan is designed to establish the optimal initial well spacing for the entire field. Finally as the initial development plan is completed and more details are learned about field characteristics, infill drilling (which creates a denser network of wells) is begun to produce the hydrocarbons that cannot be produced from existing wells or to produce them at a faster rate in the near term.

Technology and Equipment

Although Soviet drilling technology lags considerably that of Western countries, most of the drilling equipment, including rigs, pipes, casing, and bits, is produced in the Soviet Union. The Soviets rely on Western imports to fill specific needs such as additional drill pipe, high-pressure blowout preventers, and offshore drilling and logging equipment.

The USSR produced oil and gas drilling rigs of all types at a rate of about 500 per year in the last decade. The average service life of a Soviet rig is about six to 10 years, compared with 15 to 20 years for rigs built in the United States. Until recently, nearly all Soviet rigs were built at two plants—the Barrikady Plant in Volgograd and the Uralmash Plant in Sverdlovsk. Some 75 percent of the production has been at the Uralmash Plant. A new drilling rig plant was built in 1981 in Verkhnyaya Pyshma, north of Sverdlovsk. Productivity has risen during the past decade as improvements have been made in Soviet rig design, but there are chronic com-

---

Stages in Field Development

Exploration Drilling

● Producing well

Dry hole

Confirmation Drilling

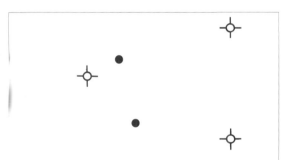

Delineation Drilling

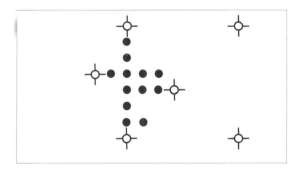

Development Drilling[a]

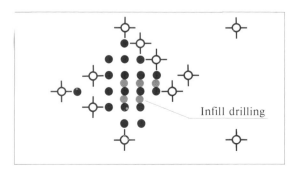

Infill drilling

[a] Based on field development plan.

Drilling Methods

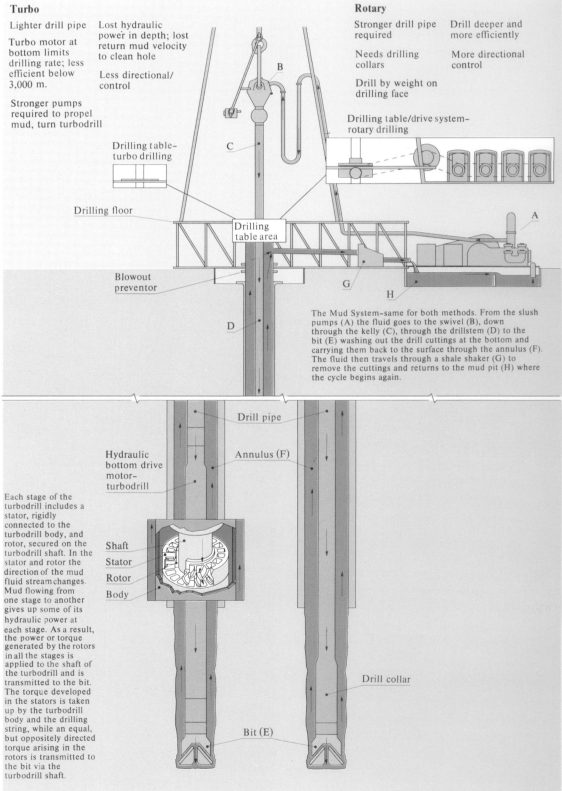

Turbo

Lighter drill pipe

Turbo motor at bottom limits drilling rate; less efficient below 3,000 m.

Stronger pumps required to propel mud, turn turbodrill

Lost hydraulic power in depth; lost return mud velocity to clean hole

Less directional/control

Rotary

Stronger drill pipe required

Needs drilling collars

Drill by weight on drilling face

Drilling table/drive system-rotary drilling

Drill deeper and more efficiently

More directional control

Drilling table-turbo drilling

Drilling floor

Blowout preventor

Drilling table area

The Mud System—same for both methods. From the slush pumps (A) the fluid goes to the swivel (B), down through the kelly (C), through the drillstem (D) to the bit (E) washing out the drill cuttings at the bottom and carrying them back to the surface through the annulus (F). The fluid then travels through a shale shaker (G) to remove the cuttings and returns to the mud pit (H) where the cycle begins again.

Drill pipe

Hydraulic bottom drive motor-turbodrill

Annulus (F)

Each stage of the turbodrill includes a stator, rigidly connected to the turbodrill body, and rotor, secured on the turbodrill shaft. In the stator and rotor the direction of the mud fluid stream changes. Mud flowing from one stage to another gives up some of its hydraulic power at each stage. As a result, the power or torque generated by the rotors in all the stages is applied to the shaft of the turbodrill and is transmitted to the bit. The torque developed in the stators is taken up by the turbodrill body and the drilling string, while an equal, but oppositely directed torque arising in the rotors is transmitted to the bit via the turbodrill shaft.

Shaft
Stator
Rotor
Body

Drill collar

Bit (E)

Directional Drilling

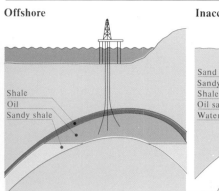

Offshore

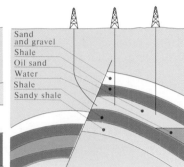

Inaccessible Locations

**Whipstock Method
for Directional Drilling**

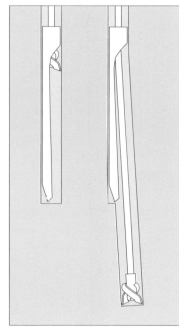

Salt Dome Control

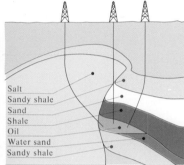

Fault Plane Control

A turbodrilling rig at Zhetybay oilfield, Mangyshlak Peninsula, North Caspian.

plaints that the mix of rig types is inadequate; especially lacking are portable rigs for use in northern climates.

Turbodrills are used for more than 80 percent of the oil and gas drilling in the Soviet Union. The turbodrill uses a downhole turbine powered by drilling mud that turns only the attached bit and not the entire drill string as does the rotary method used in the West. Turbodrills have been effective in developing the shallow, hard-rock formations in the Volga-Urals basin and for directional drilling from the cluster drilling pads in West Siberia. The original appeal of the turbodrill was that it enabled Soviet drillers to avoid many potential problems associated with

the use of low-quality domestic drill pipe and tool joints that could not withstand the stresses of rotary drilling operations. Turbodrilling eliminates torque on the drill string; consequently, it reduces the amount of time lost as a result of broken drill pipe. In addition, the turbodrill is characterized by a high rate of bit rotation which increases the initial rate of penetration. The higher rate of bit rotation in turbodrilling, however, causes a drastic shortening of bit life (meters drilled per bit), reducing the rate of penetration in deep drilling. Lost productivity caused by frequent bit changes in deep drilling increases dramatically as the drilling depth increases. The USSR now produces about 9,000 turbodrill motors annually.

The quality of Soviet drill pipe is generally adequate for drilling shallow wells (less than 2,000 meters). At greater depths, the poor-quality steel cannot withstand the torque required for rotary drilling and often fails. Even with turbodrilling, pipe inadequacies are often severe. Problems relating to the quantity and quality of drill pipe and casing produced in domestic plants have been cited as factors in the failure to meet recent West Siberian drilling targets. Moscow has been negotiating with Western firms to purchase a turnkey plant to manufacture drill pipe and casing.

The Soviet Union's output of drill bits, including standard, diamond, and experimental hard alloy types, is about 1 million per year. Although the quality and performance of Soviet drill bits improved during the 1970s, they are still much less efficient than those produced in the United States.

In 1978 the Soviets bought a turnkey drill bit plant from the United States for installation at Kuybyshev. The plant, which began operating in January 1982, is capable of producing upward of 100,000 tungsten carbide insert bits per year. At the high rotational speeds of Soviet turbo-

drills, the bits from the new Kuybyshev plant should operate for significantly longer periods than conventional Soviet-made bits, increasing productivity because of reduced downtime for bit replacement.

Administration and Organization

Three ministries—geology, oil, and gas—are responsible for drilling exploration wells. Of these, the oil and gas ministries are normally responsible for the detailed assessment of field size and potential and the drilling of development wells.

National drilling efforts by the oil and gas ministries are coordinated by Administrations for Drilling Operations. In addition, drillers are supported by research institutes in Moscow, Tyumen', and other cities. The gas ministry controls offshore drilling for both oil and gas.

The basic production unit in the Soviet oil and gas industry is the regional production association, which oversees all aspects of drilling activity including rig assembly and well completions. Drilling is conducted by drilling brigades, usually comprising 24 men, who generally operate in four teams on a single rig in shifts of up to 12 hours' duration around the clock.

Offshore Drilling

Soviet offshore drilling began nearly four decades ago in the shallow waters of the Caspian Sea. As oil and gas fields were discovered, development wells were drilled from small wooden platforms connected to the shore by trestles to facilitate movement of equipment and supplies to the drilling sites. The Caspian Sea is still the Soviet center for offshore drilling and production technology. Currently, nine of the 11 Soviet-owned and -operated mobile offshore drilling rigs are operating in the area. Offshore oil output in the Caspian is estimated at 200,000 b/d, more than three-fourths of Azerbaijan SSR's production.

By 1985 the USSR plans to boost offshore drilling activity 50 percent above the level attained in 1980. New drill ships and platforms from foreign yards and new construction in Soviet yards are part of a major effort to explore the offshore Arctic and Far East. Much of this increased emphasis on offshore drilling was stimulated by geologists' reports that potential oil-bearing sedimentary rock covers more than two-thirds of the Soviet shelf area. Development of the offshore oil potential will be important to the Soviets if they plan to maintain oil production at high levels in the 1990s. Western equipment and technology will be essential for successful development of offshore areas.

Recovery

During the past decade the Soviets have found it increasingly difficult to locate new oil reserves, to increase development drilling, and to undertake offshore exploration. As a result, the rapid production growth of the postwar period began to slow in the late 1970s. Essentially, all of the important oil-producing regions in the country are confronted with difficulties: major oilfields have been intensively exploited and have reached peak production or are in decline, new fields are less productive and more difficult to develop, and discovery of new reserves has not kept pace with the growth of oil production.

Although the Soviets produce most of their own petroleum equipment, domestic manufacturers have been unable to meet the accelerating demand of the oil industry for more and better equipment and techniques to improve oil recovery. The lack of sufficient high-quality equipment and technology has hampered efforts in several areas, including drilling in West Siberia, and the enhanced oil recovery program.

As a result of domestic production inadequacies, the USSR made selective purchases of Western equipment and technology in the 1970s. Among those oil recovery items imported were high-capacity electric submersible pumps; gas-lift equipment, including compressors and treatment units; well completion units; steam generators; and associated insulated tubing.

Various secondary and enhanced recovery techniques are necessary to offset declining production at all major Soviet oilfields.

Mechanical pumping units are commonly used to offset low reservoir pressures and lift well fluids.

Periodic servicing is required to maintain mechanical sucker rod or beam pumping units.

Workmen waiting to lower sucker rods into well.

Recovery Methods

Primary recovery is the initial production of fluids from the reservoir using natural sources of energy to produce oil and gas. Once this method can no longer cause the oil and gas to flow through the porous rocks into the wells, various secondary methods including waterflooding, mechanical pumps, and gas lift are used to recover additional amounts of oil.

In the Soviet oil industry, waterflooding is applied at a very early stage of a field's producing life to maintain reservoir pressure and to increase oil recovery. As a result, in 1980 the water content amounted to 55 percent of fluids recovered. More than 85 percent of Soviet oil output is recovered by waterflooding. The high percentage of water in the oil has increased the demand for artificial lift equipment—submersible pumps, sucker-rod pumps, and gas-lift units—to maintain or increase oil production.

Pumping units—rod or beam pumps and electric centrifugal pumps—are brought on line as wells stop flowing because of low reservoir pressure or as the amount of water in the produced fluid becomes too high. Rod pumps are used for low-flow-rate wells, while the high-capacity centrifugal pumps are used to lift large volumes of fluid. During the 1970s the USSR purchased more than 1,200 high-capacity, downhole submersible pumps from the United States. In 1983 about 60 percent of all producing wells in the Soviet Union were on rod pumps, and 20 percent were on submersible pumps.

Gas lift—a process of lifting fluids from a well by a downhole injection of gas to lighten the fluid column so that the natural reservoir energy can lift the fluid—is an alternative to high-capacity, submersible pumps, although it costs considerably more to install. Soviet petroleum officials have become more interested in the use of the gas-lift process for lifting fluids in the oilfields because of the high frequency of repairs on downhole pumping equipment. In 1969 US gas-lift equipment was installed for the first time at the Pravdinsk field in West Siberia. As a follow-on, the Soviets installed gas-lift equipment at the Uzen' oilfield in Kazakhstan and at the supergiant Samotlor and Fedorovo oilfields in West Siberia.

The Soviets are also interested in using hydraulic pumps in their artificial lift program. These pumps are submerged and are driven by high-pressure fluid from equipment at the surface, instead of being powered by electricity as are conventional submersible pumps. Although the Soviet oil industry did not use hydraulic pumps in 1980, plans call for the use of 300 such pumps by 1985.

Enhanced oil recovery (EOR) refers to recovery of oil from a petroleum reservoir beyond that economically recoverable by conventional primary and secondary methods. Three general categories of EOR are chemical flooding, carbon dioxide miscible flooding, and thermal methods.

The Soviets have expressed high hopes for EOR techniques to increase oil recovery from older fields and to produce undeveloped fields that contain heavy oil. Although they have experimented with EOR programs in many fields and tested most of the available methods, only about 60,000 b/d can be attributed to enhanced recovery at present. This yield has primarily come from the application of steam or hot water injection and in situ combustion.

Soviet EOR efforts have been hampered by severe shortages of equipment and chemicals. The Soviets have not as yet been able to build the steam generators needed for thermal recovery or to produce sufficient amounts of surfactants or polymers for chemical and polymer flood programs. Continued efforts are being made to acquire Western technical assistance and equipment to promote EOR.

Recovery Methods

Waterflooding

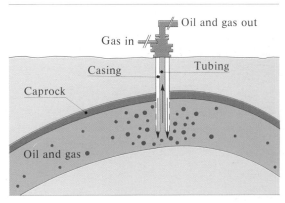

Gas Lift

Steam Flooding

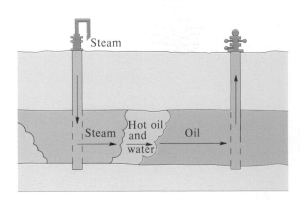

Oil Refining and Gas Processing

The rapid growth of oil and gas production in West Siberia during the 1970s has required major increases in Soviet crude-oil-refining and gas-processing capacity. Moscow is constructing new oil refineries and adding crude oil distillation units to existing refineries. A major effort is also under way to speed construction of gas-processing facilities to prepare increasing quantities of gas for domestic use and export. Although Soviet professional journals contain few production statistics, they occasionally have diagrams, flow charts, photo illustrations, and design capacities of crude oil distillation and gas-processing units.

Oil Refining

In January 1983 there were 53 oil refineries operating in the Soviet Union. Although the Soviets do not publish the total crude oil distillation capacity of these refineries, it is believed to be in the neighborhood of 10.5 million b/d, second only to the approximately 16-million-b/d capacity of the 220 operating refineries in the United States. Four-fifths of the Soviet refineries are located near population and industrial centers west of the Ural Mountains. Many of these refineries are also located within large petrochemical-refinery complexes and provide feedstocks directly to the chemical processes.

Before the mid-1950s the Soviet petroleum industry consisted of about 30 refineries with small crude oil distillation units of less-than-20,000-b/d capacity. The only secondary processing units of consequence were thermal crackers designed to break down heavy oils. Between the mid-1950s and mid-1960s a concentrated effort was made to upgrade the industry, both in crude oil distillation capacity and in secondary processing. Several standardized crude oil distillation units with capacities of 20,000 to 60,000 b/d were constructed as well as a wide variety of secondary processing units such as catalytic crackers and reformers, delayed cokers, and hydrogen treating and lubricating oil units.

With the development of the Volga-Urals oil resources in the 1950s, the Soviets stopped concentrating refineries in the crude oil production areas and began locating them near points of regional consumption, such as Omsk, Kirishi, Kremenchug, and Angarsk. The refineries receive more than 90 percent of their crude oil from pipelines; most of the remaining is delivered by rail. Conversely, only about 10 percent of the refined products are transported by pipelines; about 90 percent are delivered by rail, water, and tank truck.

Since 1970 required increases in primary distillation capacity have been obtained through modernization or expansion of existing refineries and the construction of at least five new refineries. Modernization of refineries has included the dismantling of old, small refining units and replacing them with larger, more efficient units to upgrade and improve both the output and product mix.

The Soviet refining industry is reported to have major problems in areas such as sophistication of refining processes, variety of product mix, and quality of individual petroleum products. Specifically, Soviet refineries lack adequate processing units—especially cracking units,

Section of Baku No. 2 Oil Refinery, Azerbaijan.

Oil Refineries

which break down heavier fuels into lighter fuels such as gasoline and kerosene.

The lack of adequate heavy-oil conversion capacity makes it difficult for Soviet refineries to produce high-octane gasoline and high-grade diesel fuel in the increasing volumes needed to meet growing domestic demand. Moreover, since a large share of the rising volume of heavy fuel oils cannot presently be further refined, they are primarily burned in electric power plants, thereby slowing Soviet attempts to balance fuel consumption by converting these plants to coal and natural gas.

All crude oil processed by refining must pass through an initial or primary distillation process where it is separated into gases, gasoline, kerosene, diesel fuels, and heavy fuels (mazut). These products are used as fuels or are further refined through secondary processes to produce lubricating oils, higher quality fuels, and other finished products.

Soviet refineries contain three basic types of crude oil distillation units. They range from early-design shell stills, through one-stage atmospheric pipe stills (AT), to current technology, two-stage atmospheric vacuum pipe stills (AVT). Some of the one- and two-stage units contain their own desalting section (ELOU), and some are built in combination with other types of units. The standard crude oil distillation units currently being constructed have a design capacity of 120,000 b/d.

Secondary refinery units provide a higher yield of light products and upgrade product quality after primary distillation. The most important secondary processes include reforming, catalytic cracking, hydrogen treating, hydrocracking, alkylation, and lubricating oil production. Other types of secondary processes produce specialty products, recover refinery byproducts, or treat crude oil prior to distillation or refined products prior to shipment.

Natural Gas Processing

The processing of natural gas is becoming an important subsector of the Soviet oil and gas industry after many years of neglect. In an effort to reduce the wasteful flaring of gas that is a byproduct of oil production called associated gas, the USSR is vastly expanding its capacity to produce valuable natural gas byproducts such as propane, butane, sulfur, and stable condensate. These products are useful not only as fuels but also as feedstocks in the petrochemical industry.

The rapid development of West Siberia's oilfields—especially Samotlor—outstripped the USSR's ability to process the associated gas. Flaring of the region's excess gas probably reached its peak in 1975 when about 20 billion cubic meters had to be burned off. Recently completed gas-processing plants in the Tyumen' oil region have helped reduce flaring and raised associated gas-processing capacity to nearly 20

billion cubic meters in the region during 1982. Large gas-processing facilities have been constructed at Nizhnevartovsk, Belozersk, Surgut, Yuzhno-Balyk, and Lokosovo. New processing plants in the gas-producing regions of Orenburg and Central Asia have significantly increased sulfur removal capabilities, enabling output from high-sulfur fields to replace the region's declining low-sulfur gas production.

Processing of nonassociated gas by the Ministry of the Gas Industry has grown substantially since 1970 when only 3 billion cubic meters of gas were processed. The current five-year plan calls for processing about 75 billion cubic meters of natural gas, the production of about 1.6 million tons of sulfur, and more than 20,000 b/d of gas condensate in 1985.

Natural gas is processed by several gas ministry plants located throughout the gas-producing regions. The largest and newest facility is located at Urengoy. Whether because of technological deficiencies or simply a lack of domestic production capacity, much of the gas-processing equipment is imported from the West.

Pipelines

The USSR has greatly expanded its pipeline network in recent years to transport oil and natural gas. The total length of oil and gas pipelines grew from fewer than 70,000 kilometers in 1965 to more than 231,000 kilometers by the end of 1983. During this period an average of about 6,000 kilometers of natural gas pipelines and 2,600 kilometers of oil pipelines were constructed each year.

The development of major new oil and gas fields at great distances from the economic heartland and increased gas exports are largely responsible for the massive Soviet pipeline construction program. Moscow has given high priority to the construction of pipelines from West Siberia to the industrialized areas of the USSR and to its border with Eastern Europe. At present 12 natural gas pipelines and five oil pipelines transport oil and gas from the producing areas of West Siberia.

Most pipelaying in West Siberia is accomplished when the ground is frozen during October through May. The Soviet press has emphasized the necessity of year-round pipelaying, but construction in swampy areas during the summer has been achieved only on a small scale. Activity in summer is primarily limited to areas of hard ground.

Relatively few pipelines have been built in the area of continuous permafrost. These few—the gas pipelines from the Medvezh'ye and Urengoy fields to Nadym and from Messoyakha to Noril'sk—are being built above ground to avoid trenching in permafrost and to prevent disruption of the permafrost by heat from pipelines.

Oil Pipelines

The USSR relies on pipelines to transport more than 90 percent of its crude oil production. About 83 percent of the Soviet Union's oil pipelines carry crude oil. The remaining pipelines transport refined products.

Most of the Soviet oil pipeline network is relatively new. Its growth has been dramatic—from 4,000 kilometers at the end of World War II to about 76,200 km in 1983—with half of the growth occurring between 1970 and 1983. About 20,000 km, including nearly 80 percent of the large-diameter 1,020-mm and 1,220-mm lines, were built during the 1970-80 period.

Crude oil pipeline construction has slackened appreciably in the 1980s, primarily as a result of slower growth in oil production. Only 9,200 km are scheduled for completion in the 1981-85 plan, and just two of the 16 planned pipelines are large-diameter interregional oil transmission lines: one from Pavlodar to Chimkent, completed in March 1983, and one from Kholmogory to Kuybyshev, scheduled for construction in 1984. During 1976-80, in contrast, the Soviets laid a number of major interregional lines: Nizhnevartovsk to Kuybyshev, Krasnoyarsk to Irkutsk, Kuybyshev to Kremenchug, and Surgut to Po-

lotsk. All of these lines were 1,020 or 1,220 mm in diameter.

Unlike large-diameter gas pipeline construction, the Soviet oil pipeline industry is largely self-sufficient and does not depend on Western

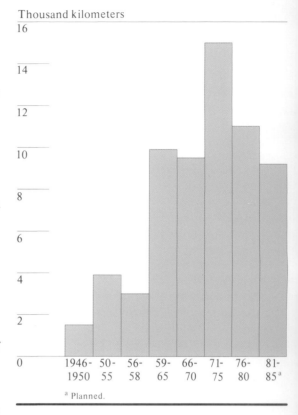

USSR: Completion of Crude Oil Pipelines, by Plan Period

Thousand kilometers

[a] Planned.

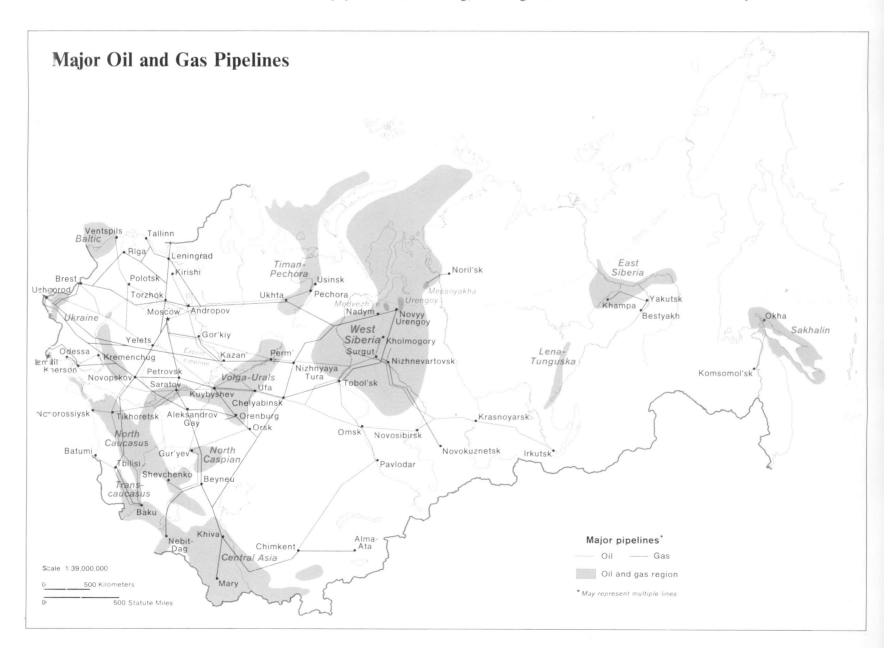

Major Oil and Gas Pipelines

Major pipelines*

— Oil — Gas

Oil and gas region

* May represent multiple lines

Scale 1:39,000,000

0 500 Kilometers

0 500 Statute Miles

USSR: Pipeline Transport of Crude Oil-Average Distance

Thousand kilometers

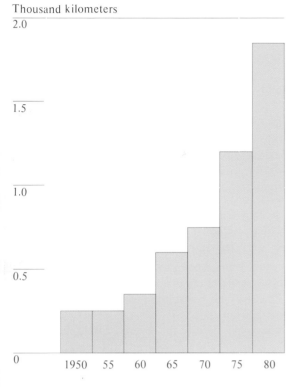

USSR: Length of Crude Oil Pipeline Network, by Diameter of Pipe

Thousand kilometers

Diameter in millimeters
- 1,020-1,220
- 530-820
- Less than 530

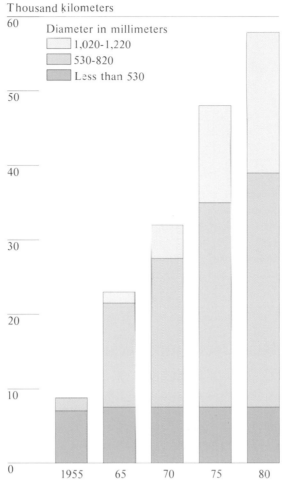

USSR: Length of Natural Gas Pipeline Network, by Diameter of Pipe

Thousand kilometers

Diameter in millimeters
- 1,420
- 1,020-1,220
- Less than 1,020

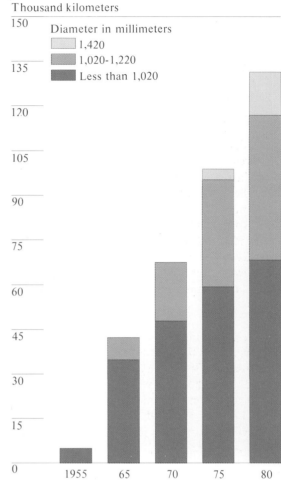

equipment and materials. Nevertheless, the Soviets do selectively import pipelayers, bulldozers, valves, and insulating materials to speed construction and to improve the operational capability and service life of their pipelines.

Gas Pipelines

Several major natural gas pipeline corridors link the gas-rich regions of West Siberia, Central Asia, and the southern Urals with the industrial centers of the European USSR. The geographic distribution and large capacity of these domestic trunklines also provide a flexible network for gas exports to the West. New pipelines under construction represent a major extension of the Soviet gas transmission system, which has grown rapidly from 2,300 km in 1950 to 155,000 km at the end of 1983. Additional gas pipelines are scheduled for completion during 1984-85.

During the current five-year plan (1981-85), four large-diameter (1,420-mm) natural gas pipelines from the Urengoy field in West Siberia have been constructed, and two more are scheduled for completion. The fourth line completed during the plan, the much-publicized Siberia-to–Western Europe export pipeline, was reportedly partially operational in early 1984, and pipelaying on the fifth domestic line is complete. The operation of the six pipelines will bring to 12 the number of large-diameter gaslines transporting gas from West Siberia.

The addition of the six new pipelines involved building some 20,000 kilometers of main trunk pipelines and will allow the Soviet Union to transport the more than 350 billion cubic meters per year of West Siberian gas production planned by 1985 (200 billion cubic meters more than in 1980). Also planned for completion during the 1981-85 period is a pipeline to transport gas condensate from Urengoy to Surgut.

Pipe is welded at storage area welding bases along the pipeline by crews using either manual arc techniques or semiautomatic units.

While the majority of the new large-diameter gas pipelines will be constructed with domestically produced pipe and compressor station equipment of less-than-desired quality and reliability, the gas network will still have a first-rate array of Western equipment. The ambitious Soviet plans to increase gas production and transport capabilities envisage reduced reliance on imported pipe and should benefit from the new multilayer pipe production plant at Vyksa, southwest of Gor'kiy.

Every year the USSR lays gas pipeline twice as long as the trans-Alaskan oil pipeline.

Coal

Coal follows oil and natural gas as a primary energy source in the Soviet Union. The Soviet coal industry dates back to the early 19th century. It remained the cornerstone of the Soviet energy industry and provided the Soviets fuel for their economic development and industrial growth until well into the Khrushchev era, when it was gradually eclipsed by oil and gas—a phenomenon that was simultaneously occurring in the United States and Western Europe. Today, the Soviet coal industry still employs more than a million workers and provides nearly 40 percent of the fuel used to generate electricity.

Most experts agree that abundant reserves will keep the Soviet Union self-sufficient in coal for the near future. Internationally, the USSR is second only to the United States in reserves and annual production of coal. Most energy specialists believe that potential Soviet coal reserves are the largest in the world.

Although coal's share of Soviet primary energy production dropped from two-thirds in 1950 to just over 50 percent in 1960 and to only 22 percent in 1983, coal remains critically important to the Soviet economy. With the cost of oil production rising rapidly, Soviet energy planners have become aware that coal must play a greater role in the total Soviet energy balance. They acknowledge, however, that investment in the coal industry has recently been insufficient both to develop new coal basins and to forestall production declines in older basins. Although

substitution of coal for oil is a high Soviet priority, the Soviet coal industry will be poorly equipped to increase production sharply, at least through the 1980s.

Coal at a Glance

Reserves	
Explored	281 billion metric tons
World rank	Second
Production	
Record year	1978—724 million metric tons
World rank	Third
1983	716 million metric tons
By coal rank	Hard coal (anthracite and bituminous), 78 percent; lignite, 22 percent
By type of mining	Surface, 40 percent; underground, 60 percent

Resources and Reserves

As of 1 January 1983 the Soviet Union estimated its coal resources at 6.8 trillion tons, about half of the world's total and nearly twice that of the United States. Only 4 percent of this total has been explored. Although the Soviets estimate the energy potential of their 281-billion-ton explored coal reserve to be four times greater than the combined potential of their oil and natural gas reserves, the easily accessible coal reserves of the European USSR have been

seriously depleted and the remote Siberian reserves are proving to be much more expensive to develop. The portion of total reserves comprised by coking coal is also enormous—estimated at 65-70 billion tons.

Soviet coal reserves are widely dispersed. In the European USSR, the Donets basin contains high-quality anthracite and bituminous coal, much of which is suitable for coking and is close to major blast furnaces. However, increasing mine depths, thinness of coal seams, and high methane concentrations are making the Donets reserves increasingly difficult to exploit. Although production has fallen as a result, the Donets basin still accounts for almost 30 percent of total Soviet coal production. The lignite reserves in the European USSR, although high in moisture, sulfur, and ash content, have, until recent years, been successfully exploited because of their closeness to centers of consumption. The Pechora coal basin, the northernmost basin in the European USSR, has also been extensively developed, despite the severe climate, because of its proximity to markets and the high quality of its bituminous coking coals.

Nearly 75 percent of the Soviet Union's explored coal reserves is located east of the Ural Mountains—thousands of kilometers from the major industrial and population centers of the European USSR. In addition to the costly mine-to-market transportation problems involved, the quality of many of these remote coal reserves is poor because of undesirable levels of ash, water, and sulfur.

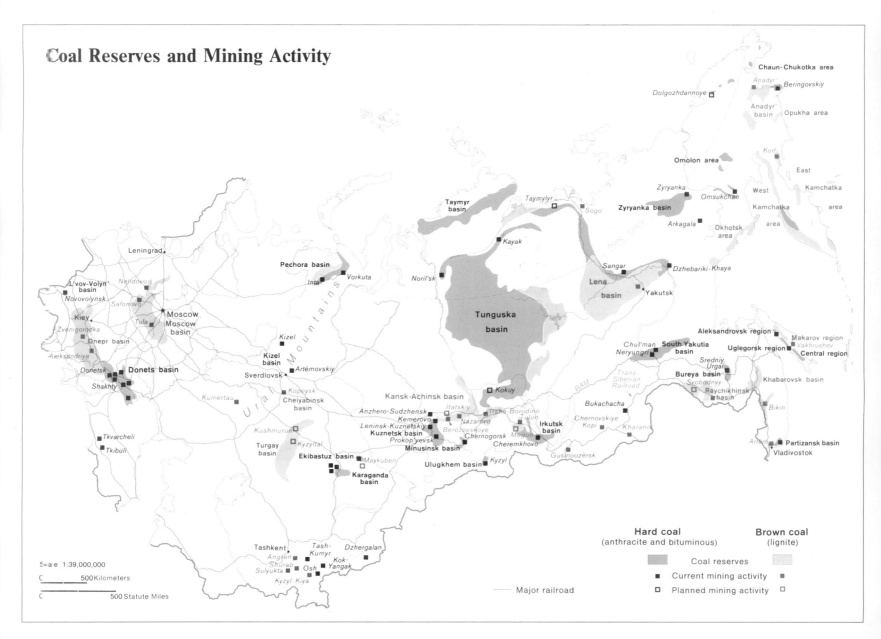

Coal Reserves and Mining Activity

Hard coal (anthracite and bituminous)	Brown coal (lignite)
Coal reserves	
Current mining activity	
Planned mining activity	

Major railroad

Scale 1:39,000,000

Until plant at Krasnoyarsk is completed, continued acquisition of foreign-made automated surface mining equipment will be required for development of eastern coal reserves.

Coal Resources

Billion metric tons

	Geological Resources	Economically Exploitable Reserves [a]	
		Probable/ Possible	Explored
Total USSR	**6,806**	**5,609**	**281**
Hard coal [b]	4,649	3,823	171
Lignite	2,157	1,786	110
European USSR (including Urals)	**473**	**218**	**76**
Hard coal	378	179	66
Lignite	95	39	10
Donets basin	141	108	56
Moscow basin	16	NA	NA
Pechora basin	265	61	NA
Kazakhstan	**170**	**121**	**25**
Hard coal	65	37	16
Lignite	105	84	9
Ekibastuz basin	10	7	7
Karaganda basin	45	25	NA
Turgay basin	51	48	6
Central Asia	**44**	**38**	**4**
Hard coal	37	33	1
Lignite	7	5	3
Siberia and Far East	**6,119**	**5,232**	**176**
Hard coal	4,169	3,574	88
Lignite	1,950	1,658	88
Irkutsk basin	77	33	7
Kansk-Achinsk basin	638	484	75
Kuznetsk basin	637	548	66
Lena basin	1,647	1,539	4
South Yakutia basin	44	40	4
Tunguska basin	2,299	1,967	2

[a] With present technology.
[b] Includes anthracite and bituminous coal.

Source: *Zapasy Ugley Stran Mira*, Moscow, Nedra 1983, pp. 93-102.

Among explored reserves in the eastern USSR, Kuznetsk and Kansk-Achinsk in Siberia are the two largest basins, but Ekibastuz and Karaganda in Kazakhstan also contain relatively small but productive reserves. Siberia's Kuznetsk basin, the Soviet's second-largest producer—after Donets—of both steam and coking coal, contains significant quantities of high-grade bituminous coal reserves with low ash and sulfur content. East of Kuznetsk and astride the Trans-Siberian Railroad, the Kansk-Achinsk basin contains huge lignite reserves. These coals, however, have a high moisture content and a low thermal energy content. Because the Kansk-Achinsk reserves are under shallow overburdens, they can be easily strip mined. The Soviets believe the Kansk-Achinsk deposit has the potential to become the USSR's largest coal-producing area by the year 2000.

Kazakhstan's coal reserves are concentrated in two basins, Ekibastuz and Karaganda. Although high in ash content, Ekibastuz subbituminous coal is an important source of steam coal for thermal power plants. Much of Karaganda's bituminous coal is used for coking.

In return for coking coal, Japan is helping the Soviet Union develop the smaller but higher quality and strippable reserves of the South Yakutia basin in Eastern Siberia. Exploitation of other large Siberian reserves will probably not begin in this century because of undeveloped rail transportation within the region and the inferior quality of the reserves. The huge Siberian coal-bearing areas of Lena and Tunguska basins represent unexplored reserves that will probably not be of commercial significance in the near future.

Production and Consumption

Between 1950 and 1975 the Soviets were notably successful in raising coal production. Annual output normally increased by an average of 4 percent each year, and production had reached more than 700 million tons by 1975. From the mid-1970s into the early 1980s, however, the Soviet coal industry experienced a leveling off and, subsequently, an actual decline in coal production. The record 1978 coal output of 724 million tons slipped to 704 million tons in 1981, then rose again to 718 million tons in 1982, but fell back to 716 million tons in 1983.

With the notable exception of the Ekibastuz basin in northern Kazakhstan, coal production from all major Soviet basins has been stagnant or in decline during much of the past decade. Production in the Donets basin—the country's largest producer of high-quality steam and met-

allurgical grade coal—is declining despite repeated Soviet efforts to maintain output. Donets production dropped by 29 million tons from its record 1978 level to 196 million tons in 1983. Output also fell in the smaller basins near Moscow and in the Urals. Together, annual production in western coal basins fell by about 32 million tons between 1977 and 1983.

Soviet planners had not anticipated a decline in production from the older basins so soon. The 1976-80 plan called for production to increase at the Donets basin by 10 million tons and at the Kuznetsk basin by 25 million tons; scheduled production at the Moscow and Karaganda basins was to remain unchanged. The plan succeeded only at Karaganda. The Soviets clearly hoped that declines in aggregate production from the older coal basins could be forestalled at least until the late 1980s, when the new coal basins of the eastern USSR would begin produc-

USSR: Coal Production Rank, 1980

Million metric tons/Percent

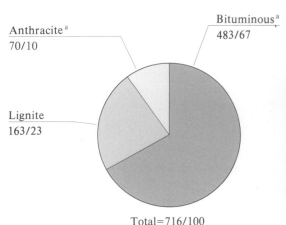

Anthracite[a]
70/10

Bituminous[a]
483/67

Lignite
163/23

Total=716/100

[a] Anthracite/bituminous breakdown is estimated.

Coal Production by Western and Eastern Basins

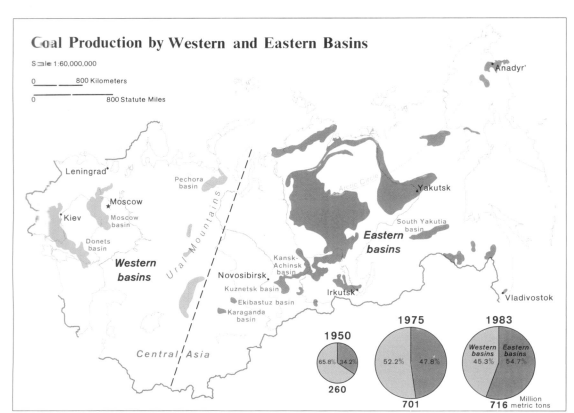

Scale 1:60,000,000

0 — 800 Kilometers

0 — 800 Statute Miles

USSR: Coal Consumption, 1980[a]

Percent

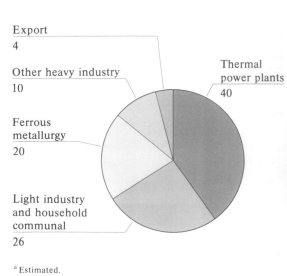

Export
4

Other heavy industry
10

Ferrous metallurgy
20

Light industry and household communal
26

Thermal power plants
40

[a] Estimated.

Coal Production, by Basin [a]

Million metric tons

Basin	1950	1955	1960	1965	1970	1975	1980	1981	1982	1983	1985 [b]
Total	260	390	510	578	624	701	716	704	718	716	775
Western USSR	171	255	327	351	355	366	338	326	330	324	341
Donets	95	141	188	206	217	223	204	198	200	196	210
Moscow	31	40	43	41	36	34	25	22	23	21	20
Pechora	9	14	18	18	21	24	28	28	28	28	28
Urals	33	47	59	62	54	45	44	43	44	44	45
Other	3	13	19	24	27	40	37	35	35	35	38
Eastern USSR	89	135	183	227	269	335	378	378	388	392	434
Ekibastuz		2	6	14	23	46	67	68	70	72	84
Karaganda	16	25	26	31	38	46	48	49	49	49	50
Kuznetsk	38	58	84	96	113	138	144	144	148	147	154
Kansk-Achinsk	2	4	9	14	18	28	35	35	37	40	48
South Yakutia						0	3	3	4	4	12
Other	33	46	58	72	77	77	81	79	80	80	86

[a] The eight largest coal basins account for more than 83 percent of annual coal production in the Soviet Union. Two of these basins, Donets and Kuznetsk, produce nearly 48 percent of Soviet coal.
[b] Soviet five-year plan.

tion. Moscow must now recognize that its planned 1985 output of 775 million tons is overly optimistic.

At least four major problems are hampering Soviet coal production:

• Conditions in underground mines are deteriorating rapidly, mine depth is increasing, seam thickness is decreasing, and methane concentrations are rising, particularly in the Donets and Kuznetsk basins. These basins account for about 50 percent of total coal production and about 75 percent of coking coal output.

• Too little new capacity is coming on line to offset the stagnating or declining production in older coal basins.

• Shortages of labor and declines in productivity are becoming more acute, especially in the older coal basins in the western USSR.

• Development of the large basins east of the Urals is constrained by the poor quality of some deposits, slow progress of research on coal preparation, lack of transportation capacity for movement of coal, and unresolved technical problems relating to long-distance transmission of electricity from mine-mouth power stations to areas of consumption.

Oil and natural gas have replaced coal in many applications in industry, transport, and the household-communal sector. Nonetheless, about 40 percent of annual coal production is burned in thermal power plants, compared with about 70 percent in the United States. Ferrous metallurgy accounts for about one-fifth of total consumption—roughly the same share as Western Europe—with other industrial users, exports, and the household-communal sector accounting for the remainder.

Moscow expects that coal's share of total Soviet energy consumption will continue to decline through the 1980s. After supplying about 70 percent of the fuel used in power plants in 1960, coal accounted for just more than 40 percent in 1980. Although coal-fired plants are being built to meet increased energy needs east of the Urals and Central Asia, there has been only a limited effort to convert oil-fired power plants to coal.

Much of the coal mined in South Yakutia's newly developed Neryungri deposit will be exported to the Far East.

USSR: Metallurgical or Coking Coal Production, by Basin [a]							*Million metric tons*
Basin	1950	1955	1960	1965	1970	1975	1980
Total	**52.0**	**78.0**	**110.0**	**139.0**	**164.8**	**180.7**	**178**
Donets	28.4	44.4	64.9	80.4	84.3	88.5	74
Kuznetsk	14.9	21.4	28.5	37.5	46.9	56.1	60
Karaganda	5.5	6.7	8.3	11.0	16.9	18.1	22
Pechora	0.2	0.9	3.8	5.2	12.1	14.1	18
Other	3.0	4.6	4.5	4.9	4.6	3.9	4

[a] Four of the eight major basins provide 98 percent of the metallurgical or coking coal mined.

USSR: Selected Characteristics of Major Coal Deposits

Deposit	Type of Coal	Type of Mining	Thickness of Seam (meters)	Average Depth of Mine (meters)	Average Calorific Value (kilocalories/ kilogram)	Moisture Content (percent)	Ash Content (percent)
Donets	Anthracite, bituminous	Underground	0.9	602	6,056	6.5	19.2
Moscow	Lignite	Underground	2.5	135	2,528	32.3	35.5
Pechora	Bituminous	Underground	2.4	487	5,217	8.3	25.1
Ekibastuz	Subbituminous	Surface	10-40		4,028	7.7	50.0
Karaganda	Bituminous	Underground	2.5	418	5,139	7.5	28.8
Kuznetsk	Bituminous	Underground and surface	2.5	262	5,550	10.2	19.0
Kansk-Achinsk	Lignite	Surface	8.7	283	3,606	33.0	10.7

Mining and Technology

The Soviet coal industry comprises nearly 900 mines located throughout the country. Although approximately 60 percent of annual coal output is currently mined underground, the Soviets expect most new production to come from large surface mines in the eastern regions, chiefly from Ekibastuz, Kuznetsk, Kansk-Achinsk, and South Yakutia.

Eighty-five percent of underground mining is done by mechanized longwall mining systems, as opposed to the room-and-pillar mining system most commonly used in the United States. Surface mining principally involves open pits with various kinds of excavators. Dipping coal seams in many of the shallow deposits, however, prevent widespread use of contour strip mining.

To date, the Soviets have given little priority to reclamation and reforestation of lands that have been surface mined.

Although the level of mechanization is fairly high, Soviet coal-mining technology is generally less advanced than that in the West. This is especially true of surface-mining technology; for example, the largest domestically produced dragline buckets, trucks, and transporters are much smaller than their Western counterparts. For this reason, substantial amounts of surface-mining equipment must be imported, principally from East Germany. Although domestically produced coal excavating equipment is available, such as the surface mining machine plant being constructed at Krasnoyarsk, the Soviets still expect to import more advanced foreign-made equipment to process South Yakutia coal.

According to the Soviets, mine conditions—dust suppression, drinking water, lighting, and underground transportation of miners—are poor. Although health and accident statistics are not published, the Soviet coal industry is known to have a mediocre mining safety record compared with that of the United States.

To mine coal from deep and diffuse deposits, the Soviets are experimenting with alternate fuel extraction and transport methods. At Belovo in the Kuznetsk basin and also in the Donets basin, for example, some coal is mined by hydraulic methods; a pipeline for transporting the resultant coal slurry from the Belovo mine some 250 kilometers to Novosibirsk is under construction.

Mining Methods

Underground Mining

Longwall Mining

Room-and-Pillar Mining

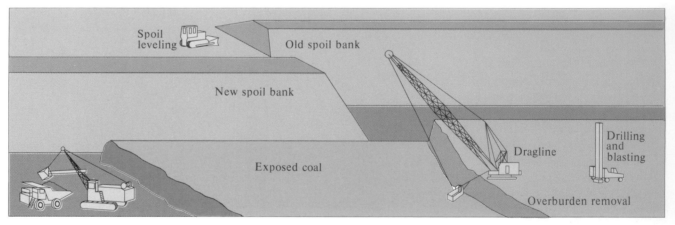

The longwall mining system is the principal underground technique used in the Soviet Union.

Surface Mining

In surface mining, the earth is excavated to uncover the coal seam. The overburden is dumped in a previously mined area. In open pit surface mining, the overburden is piled beyond the actual mining area.

Room-and-pillar mining technique seen at Donets basin mine.

The mechanized longwall mining system is the principal technique used in the Soviet Union.

Processing and shipping facilities above the Pechora underground Vorgashor coal mine, Komi ASSR.

A rotor excavator at the Ekibastuz coal basin.

P-1600 belt reloader being assembled at Ekibastuz.

Surface mining in Ekibastuz basin. The East German ERShRD-5000 powerful bucket-wheel excavator can remove 5,000 tons of coal per hour.

Transportation

The transport of coal from mining to consuming areas is a major problem for the Soviet Union. As coal reserves located near industrial centers in the western USSR have been increasingly depleted and the Soviets have been forced to go farther east to develop new reserves, the burden on the rail network has intensified. Coal is the leading freight item in terms of ton-kilometers on Soviet railroads; more than 95 percent of annual coal production is transported by rail.

Coal traffic is particularly heavy in West Siberia, northern Kazakhstan, and the Urals, as well as in parts of the Volga region and the Ukraine. In these regions much of the coal traffic must be channeled through a few already overburdened rail lines. The amount of coal shipped by rail from the Kuznetsk, Karaganda, and Ekibastuz basins to the Urals and beyond has more than doubled in the past decade to about 15 percent of total Soviet coal production. As a result, traffic slowdowns occur frequently, especially during late summer when harvested agricultural goods compete for space.

Crosshauling of fuels also adds to the burden of the railroads. Although large amounts of coal from the Kuznetsk basin in West Siberia are carried to power plants in the Ukraine, for example, coal from the Donets basin in the Ukraine is freighted to power plants in the Volga region, which is nominally within the Kuznetsk basin marketing zone. This is mainly a consequence of boiler design: the boilers in the

Various sizes and grades of coal are awaiting shipment to consumers at the Karaganda coal- yard, Kazakhstan.

Coal Transport

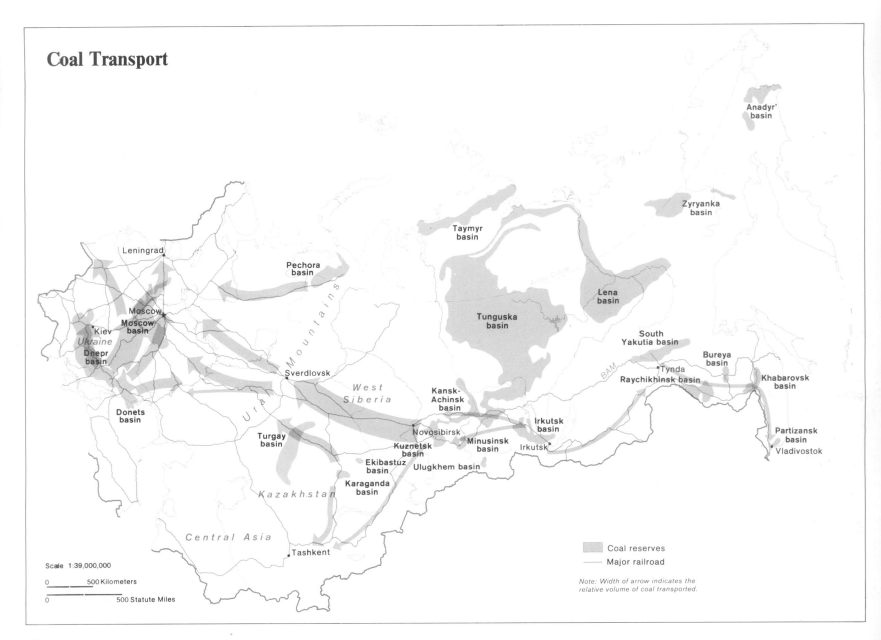

Coal reserves

— Major railroad

Note: Width of arrow indicates the relative volume of coal transported.

Scale 1:39,000,000

0   500 Kilometers

0   500 Statute Miles

A freight train transports South Yakutian coal southward to the Tynda Station on the Baikal-Amur Mainline.

Conventional Coal Slurry Pipeline System

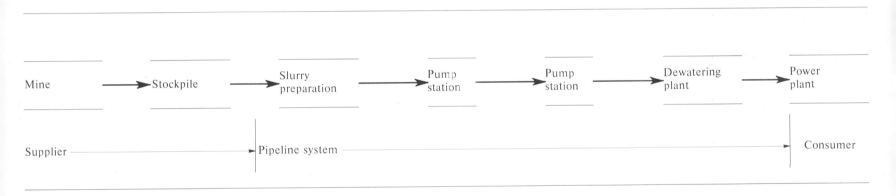

Ukraine plants that burn Kuznetsk coal were designed when similar coal was available from the Donets basin, which is now hard pressed to supply all of its former markets. To help reduce rail congestion, the Soviets plan to reequip some power plants at great cost to burn coal from closer sources. Crosshauling also occurs where coal preparation facilities are inadequate to process coal at minesites. Coal may be shipped long distances to processing plants, with associated rock and moisture adding unnecessary bulk and weight, and then shipped back to users.

Slurry pipeline transport is one of several mechanisms that Soviet engineers have proposed for movement of Siberian coal to thermal power plants in the Urals and European USSR. The Soviets have two less-than-15-kilometer slurry pipelines currently in operation in the Kuznetsk basin, and a 250-kilometer slurry pipeline from the Belovo mine in the Kuznetsk basin to Novosibirsk is reported to be under construction.

Soviet transport officials, seeking to reduce the burden on the railroads, have called for increased efforts to find new sources of coal closer to consumers. In response, Soviet officials are planning to increase production from small coal deposits in the southern Urals and in Central Asia—even though they have calculated that coal from Kuznetsk, for example, is cheaper to use in much of the European USSR than coal mined nearer by.

Inefficient railroad operating practices also contribute to fuel supply problems. For example, some 20 million tons of coal—nearly 3 percent of annual production—are lost to the economy each year, owing to underloading railcars, excessively long loading and unloading times, lack of protective coverings, and spillage from poorly maintained wooden coal gondolas. The Soviets plan eventually to have an all-metal gondola fleet.

The Soviets have particular problems dealing with coal mined in the Kansk-Achinsk fields. This coal tends to be highly pyrophoric and cannot be shipped long distances without significant risk of spontaneous combustion. Consequently, unless Kansk-Achinsk coal is processed, it must be burned in nearby furnaces and power plants.

Although Soviet transport officials stress the need to increase water transport of coal in regions of the European USSR where waterways parallel rail lines, barge transport on western rivers and canals accounts for only a small amount of coal traffic. Waterway transport, both river and coastal, is hampered by ice: virtually all waterways are frozen from three to nine months of the year. Moreover, most of the major rivers flow from south to north, which does not facilitate transport of coal from east to west.

Uranium and Thorium

The USSR has an ambitious and optimistic program for nuclear energy development. The Soviets plan to generate as much as 20 percent of their electricity from nuclear power by the year 1990 and up to 60 percent by the year 2000. Achievement of these ambitious goals will require large-scale exploitation of the nation's uranium and, to a much lesser extent, thorium resources.

Information on the Soviet uranium industry is a closely guarded state secret. Only limited data on uranium occurrences in the Soviet Union and minor details on reserves, mining, and processing operations have been published. However, according to Soviet geologic literature, almost every type of uranium deposit found elsewhere in the world has been found and exploited in the USSR. In addition, some of the uranium deposits described seem to have no Western counterparts. These include deposits associated with iron ores and albitites in Precambrian metamorphic rocks and those with phosphates in clays with detrital fishbones.

Uranium deposits in the Soviet Union are generally classified as either vein-type ores associated with metamorphic and intrusive-extrusive igneous rocks or hydrothermal deposits emplaced in sedimentary rocks. These two geologically distinct types, which seldom occur together, are

Postulated[a] USSR Total Yellowcake (U_3O_8) Production for Nuclear Power

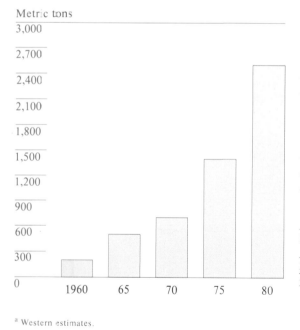

Metric tons

[a] Western estimates.

roughly of equal importance as a uranium resource.

Uranium exploration and mining methods in the Soviet Union are essentially the same as those applied in the West. Exploration methods include geologic, geophysical, geochemical, aerial radiometric, and magnetic surveys. Mining methods include:

- Underground mining to recover high-grade, vein-type deposits at a depth of 200 meters or more.
- Open pit methods applicable for low-grade ores dispersed near the surface in large areas.

USSR: Uranium-Thorium Deposits and Processing Centers

Deposit	Description
European USSR	
1-Sillamäe	Uranium-phosphate rare earth association in clays with detrital fishbones.
	Uranium mining and milling operations.
2-Zheltyye Vody–Terny	Precambrian uranium–iron ore formation.
	Irregular stratiform albitized uranium bodies.
	Uranium in association with conglomerates. Uranium minerals include uraninite, pitchblende and nenadkevite.
	Uranium mining and milling.
3-Lermontov	Uranium-molybdenum associated with volcanic rocks.
	Mining and milling operations.
4-Chupa District	Uraniferous pegmatites in Precambrian gneisses.
	Uranium mineralization in paleovolcanic and intrusive rocks of Baltic shields.
5-Lake Onega	Uranium and vanadium mineral in association with black graphitic marine shales, peat, and asphaltite.
6-Lovozero Tundra	Thorium in phosphate and rare earths in syenite complex.
	Uranium with thorium minerals in alkalic rocks.
Urals	
7-Vishnevogorsk	Uranium mineralization in nepheline syenite intrusions.
8-Novogornyy	Uranium mineralization in nepheline syenite.
Kazakhstan and Central Asia	
9-Aksuyek-Kiyakhty	Uranium mining.
10-Koktas	Uranium associated with copper mining.
11-Stepnogorsk	Possible in situ leaching of deep-seated uranium deposit.
	Uranium extraction as part of the "Tselinnyy Mining Complex."
12-Ak-Tyuz–Bordunskiy	Uranium, thorium, and rare earths associated with lead mining.
13-Chigirik	Uranium milling and processing facilities.
14-Granitogorsk	Uranium possibly associated with lead mining, milling, and concentration center.
15-Min-Kush	Uranium mining and milling operations associated with lignite in 1960s.
16-Tyuya-Muyun	Uranium-vanadium association in metamorphic limestone interlayered with volcanic tuffs and breccia.
	Tyuyamuyunite, a uranium-vanadium mineral species that was named after this locality.
17-Kyzyl-Dzhar	Uranium mining associated with gold production.
18-Kadzhi-Say	Uranium associated with lignite mining.
19-Taboshar	Uranium vanadium mining.
	U_3O_8 extraction plant.
20-Chkalovsk	Possible uranium extraction and hexafluoride conversion site for Taboshar mine ore.
21-Sumsar	Possible uranium mining.
22-Uchkuduk	Uranium associated with gold mining at Kokpatas gold mine.
	Possible uranium extraction at Navoi Mining and Metallurgical Complex.
	Ore genetically similar to South African deposits.
23-Naugarzan	Uranium-fluorite mining. Ore milling at Chigirik.
24-Charkesar	Site of former uranium mining.
25-Chavlisay–Krasnogorskiy–Yangiabad	Site of uranium mining operation.
26-Kara-Balta	Uranium processing center.
Siberia	
27-Vikhorevka	Possible uranium-thorium mining of vein-type deposits in ultrametamorphic Archean rocks.
28-Krasnokamensk	Uranium-fluorspar association in Mesozoic volcanic basins.
29-Slyudyanka	Pegmatites-uranium and rare earths.
	Mining reported in 1958 from Precambrian crystalline limestone.
30-Aldan	Uranium, thorium, and rare earths associated with gold mining.

Uranium-Thorium Deposits and Processing Centers

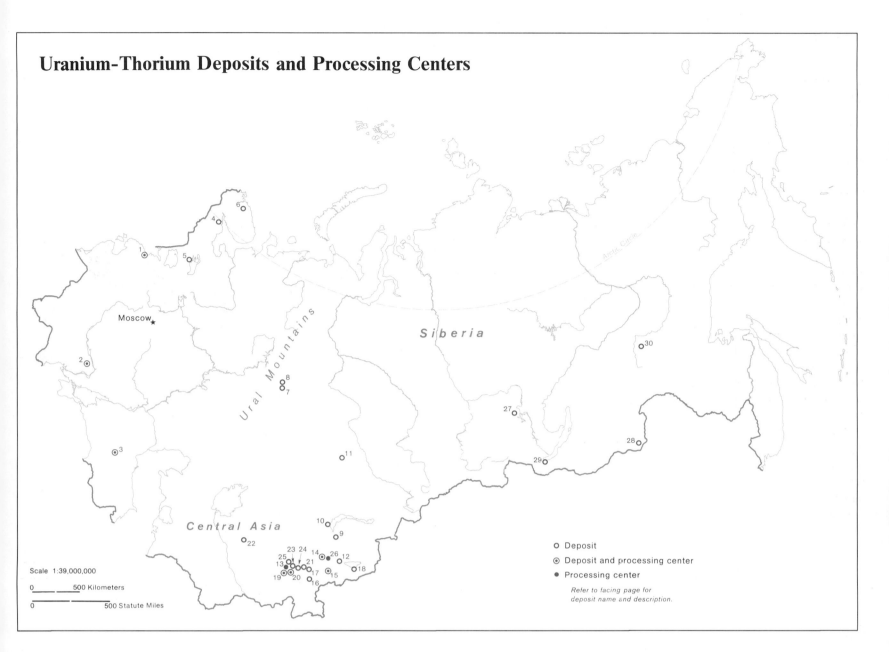

Scale 1:39,000,000

0 _____ 500 Kilometers

0 _____ 500 Statute Miles

○ Deposit
◉ Deposit and processing center
● Processing center

Refer to facing page for deposit name and description.

Production of Fissionable Materials for Electric Power Production and Military Defense

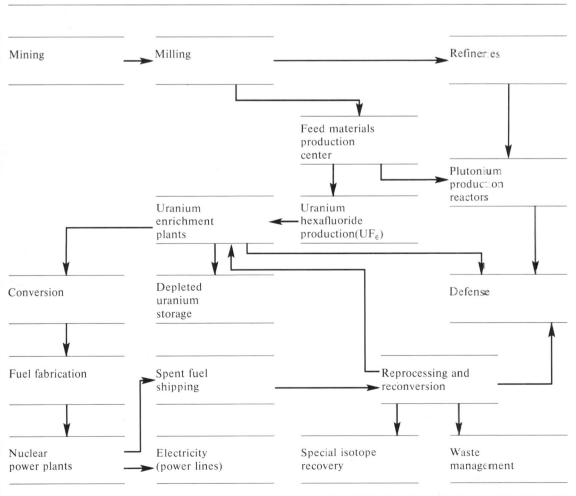

- In situ leaching techniques that use sulfuric-acidified waters to exploit low-grade deposits that cannot be mined economically by open pit or underground methods.

As elsewhere in the world, uranium milling, leaching, and concentration processes in the Soviet Union are carried out in proximity of mining operations to facilitate the separation of relatively small quantities of U_3O_8 from large volumes of ore. Information about Soviet uranium processing is even less available than that on the distribution and production of uranium. However, there are three distinct stages in processing:

- Extraction of U_3O_8 at or near the mining site.
- Conversion of U_3O_8 to uranium tetrafluoride (UF_4) by reaction with fluoride.
- Reduction of UF_4 to metal for direct use in weapons or reactor fuel or for conversion to gaseous hexafluoride (UF_6) to permit enrichment in the uranium-235 isotope.

Several alternatives to the gaseous diffusion method of uranium enrichment have received attention in the Soviet Union, including experimentation with photochemical technology using lasers.

Minor Fuel Resources

Minor fuels—oil shale, peat, and fuelwood—contributed 2 percent of total Soviet primary energy production in 1983, down from 7.2 percent in 1960. With the relative abundance of major fuel resources, production and use of the minor fuels have been largely confined to those areas of the country without close-at-hand supplies of oil, natural gas, or coal. In these areas, the Soviets have often found it more economical to burn peat, wood, and oil extracted from shale in their power plants and furnaces than to transport major fuels from distant producing regions.

The development of tar sand deposits—from which oil can be extracted—is still in the experimental stage in the USSR. Thus far, the high costs of recovery, refining, and transportation make extensive exploitation of these sands uneconomical during this century.

Oil Shale

The Soviet Union has substantial explored reserves of oil shale and leads the world in its exploitation as an energy source.[1] According to Soviet estimates, the total geological resources of oil shale in the USSR range from 190-220 billion tons. Of this amount, the Soviets believe 56 billion tons are economically recoverable using current technology. Thus far, however, only 6.5 billion tons of those reserves are in explored deposits.

The Estonian and Leningrad oil shale fields near the Baltic Sea, with 5 billion tons of explored shale reserves, yield about 97 percent of all Soviet production. In 1980 the Estonian field alone accounted for nearly 84 percent of the oil shale mined in the USSR. Currently, the only other commercial oil shale deposit is the Kashpirovka field near Syzran' on the Volga River.

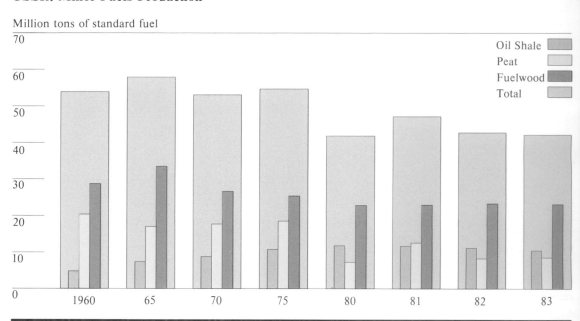

USSR: Minor Fuels Production

Million tons of standard fuel

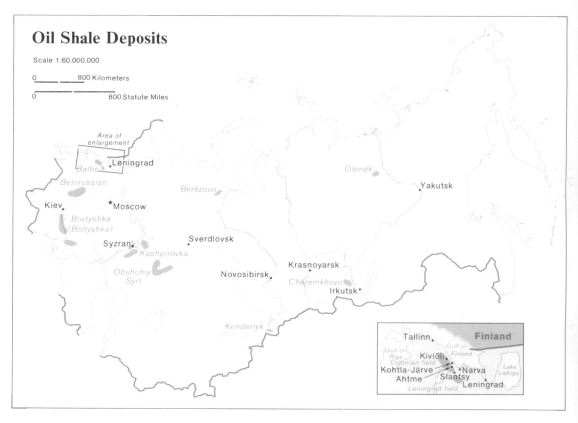

Oil Shale Deposits

Scale 1:60,000,000

Loading oil shale at Oktyabr' mine, Estonia.

In Estonia, oil shale has been used since the 1920s as fuel in various types of industrial furnaces and in locomotives. Today, approximately 70 percent of the shale produced in the USSR is burned directly as fuel in the furnaces of boiler units at power plants in Kiviõli, Tallinn, and near Narva. The two thermal power plants near Narva—the 1,610-MW Estonian State Regional Electric Power Plant (GRES) and 1,435-MW Baltic GRES—are the world's largest power plants that burn this fuel. Estonia,

[1] Oil shale is sedimentary rock rich in kerogen, a fossil organic substance that yields oil, gas, and tar when heated.

with more than 60 percent of its fuel demand supplied by shale, is the only republic of the USSR, and the only political entity in the world, where oil shale predominates in the fuel balance.

The USSR has an active and well-established industrial and technical base, with more than 50 years of experience, for mining, retorting, gasification, and direct combustion of Baltic oil shales. Virtually all current shale oil output is from 12 underground and four surface mines. Underground mining, using the room-and-pillar method, accounts for 60 percent of annual production. The nearly 30 percent of oil shale production not burned by combustion is processed at four sites located near the shale mines at Kohtla-Järve–Ahtme, Kivioli, Slantsy, and Syzran'.

The Soviet Union uses two principal types of retorts to process raw shale: gas generators and solid heat carriers. The most significant methods are the Kiviter and Galoter processes. The Kiviter process produces shale oil, shale tars, and large quantities of heating gas (low-caloric

gas) from lump shale. Until 1978 the largest gas generators could process about 400 tons of shale daily, but in that year a scaled-up Kiviter retort capable of processing 1,000 tons daily was installed near Kohtla-Järve–Ahtme at the V. I. Lenin Combine.

The Soviets refer to the Galoter process as the UTT process, and associated retort units (which have a unit maximum throughput capacity of 3,300 tons per day of Baltic oil shale) are referred to as UTT-3000 units. They first used the technique in 1980 in a pilot oil shale processing plant located adjacent to the Estonian Thermal Power Plant. The new UTT-3000 process uses solid heat retorts, and the temperature can be controlled to provide an optimum mix of oil, gas, and tars that are then either burned as fuel or further refined into numerous oil-based products. The Galoter process is the most advanced for industrial oil shale retorting in the USSR.

The Soviets also use some of the inorganic residual ash waste from the shale oil conversion process as building material and soil conditioner. Despite these beneficial uses, spent shale presents a serious disposal problem. Large areas in the shale regions of the USSR have been despoiled by shale strip mining and dumping of processing waste. Although some areas have been restored through grading and planting, revegetation of open pit mines and spent shale dump sites is difficult because of the high alkalinity of the soil.

Tar Sands

The USSR has more than 30 billion tons of potential oil reserves that could be extracted from tar sands. The largest concentration of tar sand deposits occurs in northwest Yakut ASSR. The best known of these is the Olenek tar sand deposit near the Lena River. Because of their remote location, the Soviets do not anticipate exploiting the Olenek or other East Siberian tar sands in the near future.

Currently, the Soviets have limited experimental development of tar sands to deposits in the Volga, Pechora, Transcaucasus, and Central Asia regions. The only significant Soviet oil production from tar sands comes from the Yarega field near Ukhta in the Pechora basin of northern Komi ASSR. Here, the Soviets recover heavy oils and bitumen sands via "oil mining." The oil is located at depths of 200 to 400 meters and requires heating to be recovered from seams 2 to 5 meters thick. The resulting heavy oils are refined into specialty oils, greases, and lubricants.

Peat

The USSR has about 60 percent of the world's peat resources. Soviet geologists estimate their peat reserves at about 150 billion tons, which includes 30- to 40-percent moisture content. Peat is distributed throughout much of the country, but only the reserves in the Baltic republics, the Moscow-Gor'kiy area, and Belorussia are intensely exploited at this time.

The Soviet Union is the world's largest producer of peat, both for fuel and agriculture. Current peat production in the USSR is about 230 million tons per year. About two-thirds of the peat produced is used in agriculture and by the chemical industry for the production of methanol and synthetic natural gas (SNG). Of the remaining peat, nearly 40 percent is burned in several major thermal power plants in European USSR, 10 to 15 percent is formed into briquettes for home heating, and the rest is used in industrial boilers and in large heating plants.

For many years, the use of peat as an energy source has been declining. Peat now accounts for only 0.4 percent of total energy supply. Recent Soviet studies on the future of the peat industry have concluded that the amount of peat used as fuel will continue to decrease because of insufficient reserves in the primary consuming areas and increasing demand in the agricultural sector.

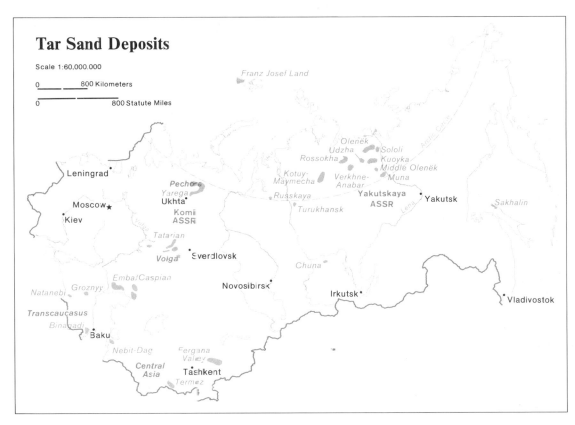

Tar Sand Deposits

Scale 1:60,000,000

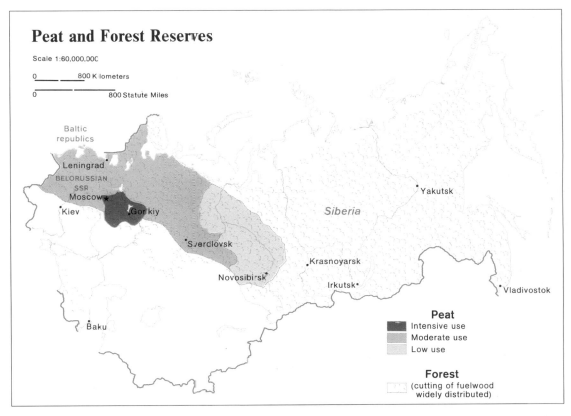

Peat and Forest Reserves

Scale 1:60,000,000

Peat
Intensive use
Moderate use
Low use

Forest
(cutting of fuelwood widely distributed)

Fuelwood

Forests cover approximately one-third of the territory of the USSR. In 1983 the lumbering industry cut 356 million cubic meters of timber, of which about 23 percent was designated as fuelwood.[2] Production of fuelwood has been slowly decreasing in recent years, but wood still comprises up to 40 percent of the locally expended fuel in the northern forest regions and is also an important fuel in the central region. Overall, wood currently contributes slightly more than 1 percent of the national energy supply.

[2] These figures do not include fuelwood gathered by the populace. Occasional data indicate that the amount may nearly equal the fuelwood cut by the lumbering industry.

Fuelwood is principally used in home heating or as feedstock in the synfuel industry; it is rarely burned in power stations. The Soviets are able to produce automotive fuels and methanol from wood fibers and waste by using an acid hydrolysis process. This synthetic fuel is produced at a small demonstration plant near Krasnoyarsk, designated the SKR-10. The Soviets are increasing the volume of wood chips exported for use in producing synfuels and plan to construct industrial plants in Siberia that can convert 2 million tons per year of wood chips and waste into 40,000 tons per year of synfuel.

Electric Power

Since 1920, when Lenin presented his dictum "Communism is Soviet power plus the electrification of the entire country," the Soviet Union has become a world leader in the generation of electric power. Virtually every settled area of the vast Soviet territory has now been electrified. But, even though the electric power base of the USSR has been growing rapidly for many years. much faster than the economy as a whole, there is still not enough electricity available to meet all Soviet industrial and communal needs.

Industry is the principal consumer of electric power. Its share of the total electricity consumption has been gradually decreasing, but still amounted to 65 percent in 1983. Compared with other countries, the transportation sector receives a relatively large share, 9 percent, and is maintaining that share as the electrification of railroads expands and the electric power requirements of oil and gas production and distribution systems increase. Plans call for the share of power allocated for household, municipal, and agricultural use to grow from 20.5 percent in 1980 to 22 percent in 1985. This should improve the power supply for domestic and communal uses, which has long been inadequate. Exports of electric power amount to only 1.7 percent of production.

Despite the rapid growth of the power industry, insufficient generating capacity in the European part of the USSR where industry and population are concentrated, leads to chronic power shortages. Provision of additional capacity is impeded by inadequate local fuel and hydro-power resources and the costs and difficulty of transporting fuel from elsewhere. As the growth rate of the labor force declines, economic growth is becoming more and more dependent on electric power to help increase labor productivity.

To increase its electric power supply, the USSR is promoting rapid growth of nuclear power and pumped-storage hydroelectric power plants in the European part of the country while continuing to build major hydropower plants on large Siberian rivers and large thermal power plants in the coal-rich eastern regions. It is also attempting to improve efficiency by concentrating power production in large regional power plants and installing larger generators. To improve the distribution of power, the Soviet Union is in the process of integrating the regional power networks via ultra-high-voltage (UHV) transmission lines to form a national power system. And it is developing alternative energy technologies to meet local small-scale and supplementary needs.

Electric Power Administration

The Soviet Ministry of Power and Electrification, in effect, controls more than 90 percent of the country's installed electric power capacity and output. The remaining generating plants are either under the administration of various other ministries, such as metallurgy, machine building, transportation, and agriculture, or assigned to local authorities or industries. Transmission, however, is controlled by the Ministry of Power

and Electrification. Like other energy ministries, the Ministry of Power and Electrification has an extensive array of subordinate enterprises and institutes, almost all of which are headquartered in Moscow.

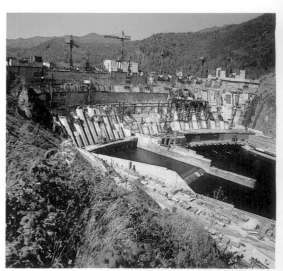

The 6,400-MW Sayan-Shushenskoye Hydropower Dam across Yenisey River, East Siberia.

Production and Consumption

The Soviet Union is second only to the United States in the generation of electric power, although per capita production lags behind that of many industrialized countries. Power generation in the Soviet Union grew from less than 500 million kilowatt-hours (kWh) in 1920 to 1.42 trillion kWh in 1983 (about half the amount

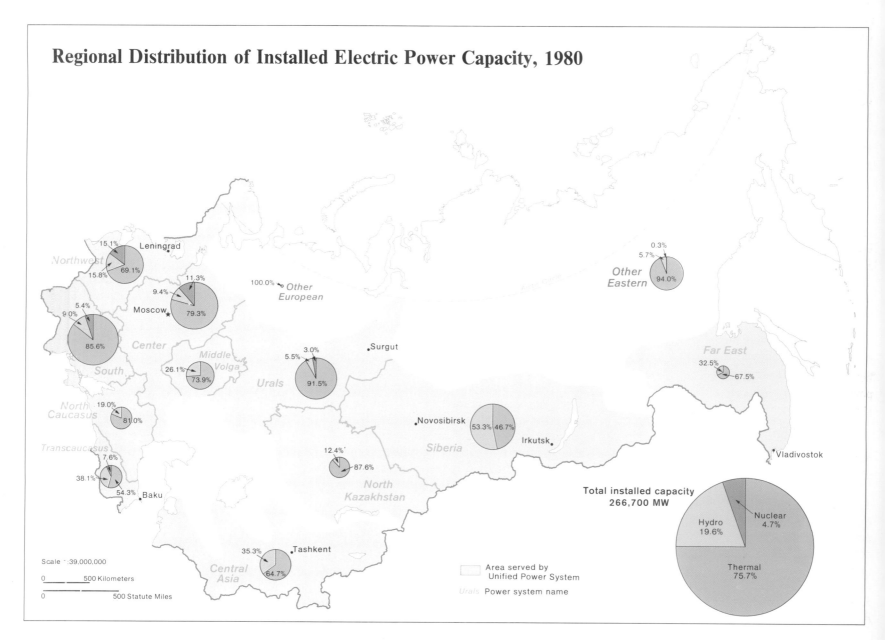

Regional Distribution of Installed Electric Power Capacity, 1980

USSR: Electric Power Acronyms

Like many American industries, the Soviet electric power industry uses acronyms for types of power plants and their components. Some of these acronyms have passed into general usage, and knowledge of them facilitates identification in Soviet publications.

Power generation

AES	Atomic/nuclear electric power plant
AKES	Atomic condensation electric power plant
AST	Atomic heat supply plant
ATETs	Atomic heat and electric power plant
DES	Diesel power plant
GAES	Pumped-storage electric power plant
GeoTES	Geothermal electric power plant
GES	Hydroelectric power plant
GRES	State regional electric power plant (thermal)
	Gas-turbine electric power plant
GTU	Gas-turbine installation
KES	Condensation electric power plant
MHD	Magnetohydrodynamic generators
MINENERGO	USSR Ministry of Power and Electrification
PES	Tidal electric power plant
PGU	Steam gas-turbine units
SES	Solar power plant
TETs	Heat and electric power plant

Power transmission

AC	Alternating current
CEMA	Council for Mutual Economic Assistance
DC	Direct current
EHV	Extra-high-voltage (330- to 750-kV AC and 800-kV DC)
ES	District power system
GOELRO	State Plan for Electrification of the Soviet Union (1920)
GOSTANDART	State Committee for Standards
HV	High voltage (35- to 220-kV AC)
kV	Kilovolt
kW, kWh	Kilowatt, kilowatt-hours
LEP	Long-distance transmission line
MW	Megawatt
OES	Consolidated regional power system
VL	Overhead line
TEK	Fuel and power complex (KATEK—Kansk-Achinsk Fuel and Power Complex)
UHV	Ultrahigh voltage, voltages greater than 750-kV AC or 800-kV DC (1,150-kV AC and 1,500-kV DC)
LEP-500	Overhead transmission line (number indicates voltage)
USSR YeES	Unified Power System of the Soviet Union

Installed Capacity of Electric Power Plants

Thousand megawatts

	1960	1965	1970	1975	1980	1983	1985 Plan
Total	**66.7**	**115.0**	**166.2**	**217.5**	**266.7**	**293.6**	**327.6**
Nuclear	NEGL	0.3	0.9	4.7	12.5	20.2	33.8
Hydro	14.8	22.2	31.4	40.5	52.3	57.0	64.7
Thermal	51.9	92.5	133.9	172.3	201.9	216.4	229.1

Electricity Production

Billion kilowatt-hours

	1960	1965	1970	1975	1980	1983	1985 Plan
Total	**292.3**	**506.7**	**740.9**	**1,038.6**	**1,293.9**	**1,418.1**	**1,555**
Nuclear	NEGL	1.4	3.5	20.2	72.9	109.8	220
Hydro	50.9	81.4	124.4	126.0	183.9	180.4	230
Thermal	241.4	423.9	613.0	892.4	1,037.1	1,127.9	1,105

Electricity Consumption

Billion kilowatt-hours

	1960	1965	1970	1975	1980	1983	1985 Plan
Total	**292.3**	**506.7**	**740.9**	**1,038.6**	**1,293.9**	**1,418.1**	**1,555**
Industry (including construction)	216.4	361.3	503.4	678.0	799.2	NA	927
Transport	17.6	37.1	54.4	74.2	102.8	115.5	128
Communal and municipal	30.5	50.6	81.0	119.1	155.0	NA	190
Agriculture	10.0	21.1	38.6	73.8	110.9	126.6	157
Exports	NEGL	1.5	5.2	11.3	19.1	23.9	25
Line losses	17.8	35.1	58.3	82.2	106.9	115.3	128

Principal Industrial Consumers of Electric Power, 1980
Percent

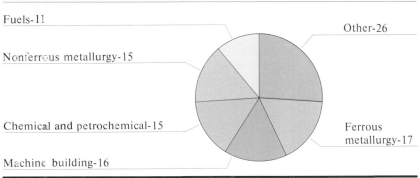

Fuels-11
Other-26
Nonferrous metallurgy-15
Chemical and petrochemical-15
Ferrous metallurgy-17
Machine building-16

---

generated in the United States). This growth was achieved through heavy investment in power plant construction: since 1960, for example, the electric power industry has been allocated about 10 percent of the total capital investment in industry.

The 11th Five-Year Plan called for the installation of 68,900 megawatts (MW) of new capacity between 1981 and 1985, which would permit power production to increase an average of 3.7 percent annually and reach 1,555 billion kWh in 1985. If production continues to grow at a 4-percent annual rate, it would reach about 2,200 billion kWh in the mid-1990s, the level reached in the United States in 1976.

To increase generating capacity at the least cost, the Soviet Union is building fewer, but bigger power stations using larger, more efficient generating units. (Large power plants are generally more cost effective than small plants in both construction and operation.) The 6,000-MW Krasnoyarsk Hydroelectric Plant on the Yenisey River in Siberia is currently the largest hydro-

electric power plant in the world, and the Sayan-Shushenskoye station, when the last two generating units are installed in 1985, will be even larger at 6,400 MW. The 4,000-MW Ekibastuz GRES-1 in Kazakhstan, which reached fully operational capacity in 1984, the 3,800-MW Reftinskiy Thermal Power Plant in the Urals, and the slightly smaller Zaporozh'ye and Uglegorsk plants in the Ukraine are among the largest thermal power plants in the world. Of the more than 900 major Soviet electric generating plants at the end of 1983, 57 were thermal power plants, 14 were hydroelectric power plants, and eight were nuclear power plants with capacities of 1,000 MW or more. These 79 large plants contributed about 163,000 MW, some 55 percent of the total Soviet power generating capacity.

The Soviet electric power industry is most developed in the European part of the country including the Urals. This region produces 72 percent of the national output of electricity. But 75 percent of the people and most of the industrial centers are located in the European USSR, and

demand for power exceeds supply during peak hours. Voltage drops and brownouts are common; moreover, demand is rising steadily. Although additional large power plants are needed to fulfill peak demand requirements, the hydroelectric potential of the European rivers has already been almost fully exploited.

East of the Ural Mountains there is a better balance between power generation and demand. Major thermal and hydroelectric power plants have been built where population and industry are concentrated, mainly along the Trans-Siberia Railroad and in the Kuznetsk basin of West Siberia. The abundant coal and hydroelectric resources permit strong growth of the electric power industry in the eastern regions; between 1980 and 1985 production was scheduled to increase by more than 40 percent in the east compared to 30 percent in the European area. Eventually, as electric power production in the eastern regions exceeds demand, the Soviets plan to transmit the surplus to the energy-short European areas via UHV transmission lines.

Thermal Power

Thermal power plants have always been the backbone of the Soviet electric power industry. In 1983 fossil-fuel-burning plants accounted for three-fourths of total Soviet power plant capacity and generated 80 percent of total electric power output.

Thermal power plants in the Soviet Union are built according to standard designs prepared by the All-Union State Institute for Planning Thermal Electric Power Stations. The generating units in these plants commonly range from 50 to 800 MW in output capacity and are combined into assemblies comprising one boiler, one turbine, one generator, and one transformer. Since 1963, when the first 300-MW units were put into operation, nearly 400 of these units have been installed, making them the standard generating units of large thermal power stations. In the last decade, twelve 500-MW units, eight 800-MW units, and one 1,200-MW unit have gone into operation. In the future, the 500-MW and 800-MW units should become the standard generating units of large thermal power plants, while 200-MW and 300-MW units will continue to be installed in medium-size power plants.

In keeping with the Soviets' shift in policy to locate power generation facilities near fuel resources, four 4,000-MW plants, each with eight 500-MW generating units, have been planned for northeastern Kazakhstan, near the Ekibastuz subbituminous coal deposits. By late 1984, all eight 500-MW units for the first Ekibastuz thermal power plant had been installed. Construction of the three additional plants at Ekibastuz and the one at Chiganak, in southern Kazakhstan, is considerably behind schedule. A similarly large plant (with eight 800-MW units) near the Berezovskoye mine in the Kansk-Achinsk brown coal basin has also been delayed and the first unit is now scheduled for startup in 1985.

State regional electric power plants (GRESs) provide central thermal power generation for large areas and for areas of high demand. At the beginning of 1983 there were 51 large GRESs with capacities of more than 1,000 MW; together they comprised almost half of the national thermal power generating capacity. Most of these large GRESs are located in European areas of the Soviet Union; among them are 12 in the Ukrainian Republic, seven in the Urals and six in the Central Moscow Power System. There are only 12 large GRESs in the eastern regions of the country—four in Central Asia, five in Siberia, and three in Kazakhstan.

The cogeneration of electric power and heat—little practiced in Western countries—is common in the Soviet Union. At present there are more than 1,000 combination heat-and-power plants (TETs) in the USSR, all located in or near urban areas or at industrial plants. Besides electricity, they supply heat to residences and other indoor facilities and process steam to industrial enterprises. Even though less electricity is obtained per unit of fuel, cogeneration is a more efficient use of fuel than generation of electricity alone, because the heat of combustion is more fully exploited.

At the end of 1983 the total electric power generating capacity of all TETs in the Soviet Union was about 75,000 MW or 35 percent of total thermal power plant capacity. The TETs produced about 375 billion kWh of electricity and 1,200.3 million gigacalories of heat, the latter fulfilling 40 percent of the heating requirements of the cities. There are 12 TETs in Moscow alone, with total capacities of 5,100 MW of electricity and 22,000 gigacalories of heat per hour. The TETs-23 in Moscow is the largest TETs in the country; it can simultaneously generate 1,400 MW of electricity and 2,140 gigacalories per hour. Throughout the Soviet Union about 17,000 kilometers of heating mains have been installed, 2,200 kilometers in Moscow alone.

The generation of electric power from internal combustion engines (for example, diesel generators) has been widespread in the Soviet Union, especially in remote areas, but this practice is decreasing because internal combustion power generation is inefficient and relatively costly. Instead, where feasible, transmission networks centered on GRESs are being extended to remote areas.

Construction of the 1,260-MW Mary Thermal Power Plant, Central Asia.

The 2,400-MW Lukoml' Thermal Power Plant, Belorussia.

Major Thermal Power Plants

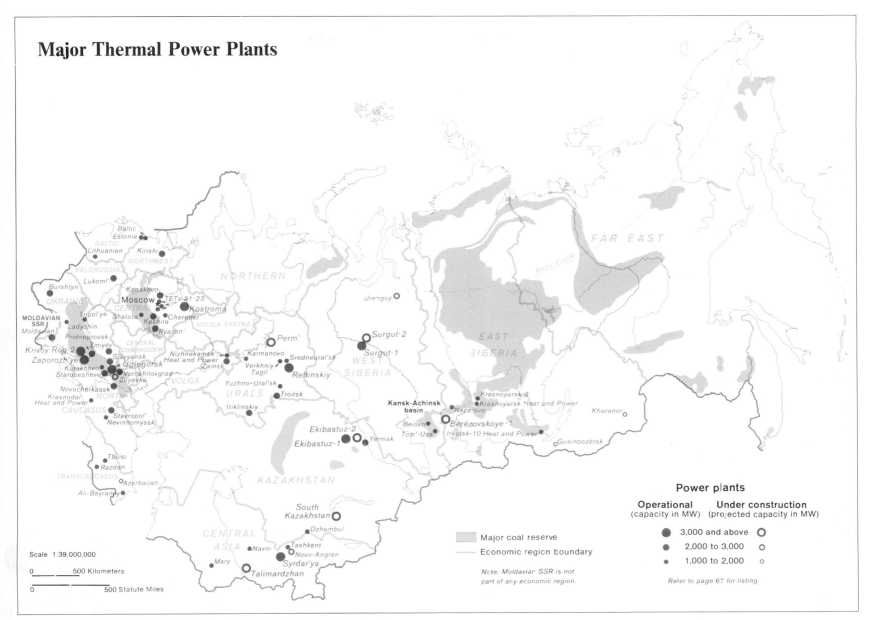

The average consumption of fuel at thermal power plants of the Ministry of Power and Electrification has been reduced through improved efficiency. This improvement in efficiency has been achieved through the replacement of many small, old generating units with fewer larger, modern units and the increased cogeneration of heat and electricity.

Coal has been the principal fuel used in thermal power plants in the USSR. In the early 1960s, however, a significant shift toward natural gas and fuel oil was initiated. At the time, these fuels were cheaper as well as cleaner than coal, and the cost of constructing a gas- or oil-fueled power plant was calculated to be significantly less than the cost of a coal-burning power plant. In the mid-1970s Soviet policies on fossil fuels changed again and coal again became the preferred fuel for Soviet power plants. Most new thermal power plants are gas or coal fired; very few oil-burning plants are being built. To conserve oil, some oil-burning power plants in the Urals and Volga regions have been converted to burn gas piped from the large West Siberian gas deposits. Because of a tight coal supply, even some coal-fired plants are being converted partly to gas.

Because they are usually located in cities, most TETs will continue to burn oil and gas, which produce fewer pollutants than coal. Currently, the primary method of controlling atmospheric pollutants (mainly sulfur dioxide and ash) from thermal power plants is the use of very tall smokestacks which disperse the effluents into the higher layers of air.

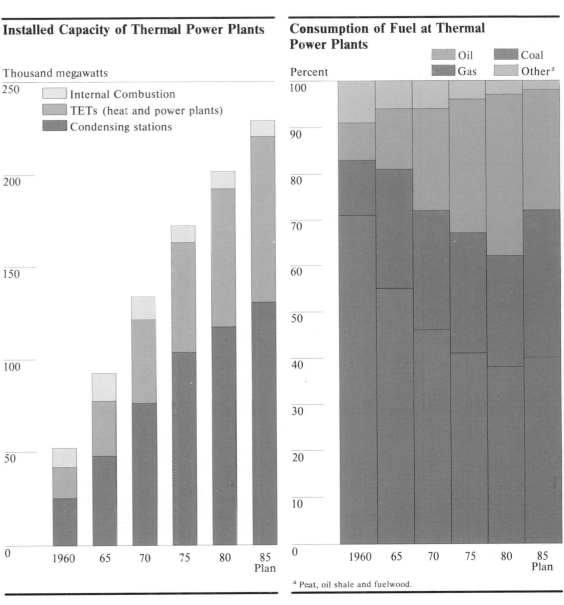

49

Hydroelectric Power

Resources

The Soviet Union has huge hydroelectric resources; only China has more. The Soviets have calculated that the economically exploitable portion of these resources has a potential generating capacity of 270,000 MW that could theoretically provide 1,095 billion kWh of electricity annually. Only 20 percent of that potential

USSR. The European share, however, is decreasing as large new hydropower plants are completed in the eastern regions. About two-thirds of the 12,400 MW of new hydropower generating capacity planned for 1981-85 was to be installed in eastern regions of the country.

The more than 400 hydropower stations administered by the Ministry of Power and Electrification account for virtually all Soviet hydroelectric capacity. Among these stations, which range

power production has been constrained by a shortage of rainfall, increased allocations of water for irrigation, and increasing reliance on hydropower to meet peak demand.

The USSR has started building pumped-storage hydropower plants to help meet the demand for power during peak periods. The first Soviet pumped-storage plant (225-MW capacity) is already in operation on the Dnepr River near Kiev. A 1,200-MW plant is being built at

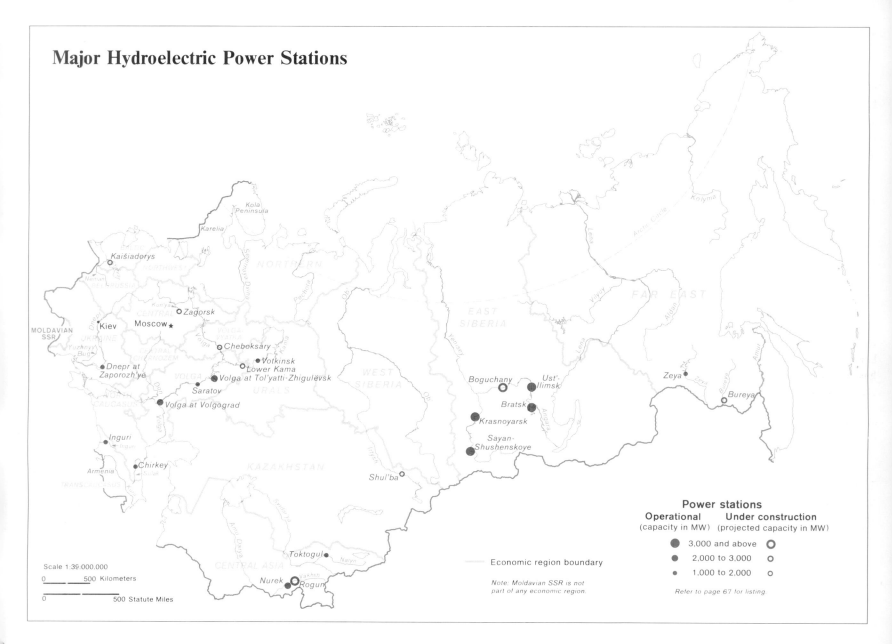

Major Hydroelectric Power Stations

Scale 1:39,000,000

0   500 Kilometers

0   500 Statute Miles

Economic region boundary

Note: Moldavian SSR is not part of any economic region.

Power stations

Operational (capacity in MW)	Under construction (projected capacity in MW)
● 3,000 and above	○
● 2,000 to 3,000	○
● 1,000 to 2,000	○

Refer to page 67 for listing.

capacity had been installed by the end of 1983. (In comparison, the United States had exploited 36 percent of its estimated 186,000 MW of potential capacity.) About 66 percent of the Soviet hydropower resources is located in Siberia and the Far East, 18 percent is located in the European part of the country, and 16 percent is located in Kazakhstan and Central Asia.

Hydroelectric Power Stations

The Soviet Union has built some of the world's largest hydroelectric power stations and, in the mountainous regions of the Caucasus and Central Asia, some of its highest dams. At the end of 1983 the total installed capacity of Soviet hydroelectric power plants was 57,000 MW, about 20 percent of total national electricity generating capacity. In contrast to the distribution of resources, about half of the installed hydropower capacity is located in the European

in size from 6,000 to less than 5 MW, are 14 with capacities of 1,000 MW or more that by themselves account for more than 60 percent of total hydroelectric capacity.

Power Production

Power output from Soviet hydroelectric plants amounted to 180.4 billion kWh in 1983, more than 14 times output in 1950. From 1950 to 1970 production grew at an average annual rate of 12 percent, but since 1970 output of hydropower plants has grown much more slowly, at an average of 2.9 percent a year. During the 1960s hydropower plants provided about 17 percent of total electric power output, but by 1983 that share had dropped to less than 13 percent. The hydroelectric share of total electric power output is expected to remain stable for the rest of the decade.

In recent years, the growth of Soviet hydro-

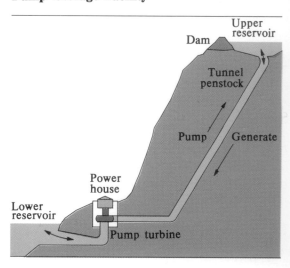
50

Zagorsk, near Moscow, and a 1,600-MW plant at Kaisiadorys, in Lithuania. Another facility under construction will be used in conjunction with the South Ukraine Nuclear Power Station near Konstantinovka, on the Yuzhnyy Bug River.

Regional Summary of Hydropower Development

The European USSR

On many of the major rivers of the European USSR—Volga, Kama, and Dnepr—the Soviets have built hydroelectric dams in series to form cascades of large reservoirs, which, in addition to providing power, combine with canals to make deepwater river transport possible between five seas. Although only 40 percent of the hydroelectric potential of the European part of the country has been exploited, most of the sites in the European area where new hydropower plants could be built are in northern regions and in the mountains of the Caucasus, far from the areas of high power consumption.

More than half of the economic hydropower potential in Soviet Europe is concentrated in the basins of the Volga, Dnepr, Kura, and Pechora Rivers. Exploitation of the Dnepr and the Volga began in the early 1930s. The Dnepr Cascade has been virtually completed; it has six hydroelectric power stations with a total capacity of 3,575 MW. The eight-station Volga Cascade is also nearly finished. The last station, the Cheboksary Hydropower Station, began generating power in late 1980. When all of its 18 units are installed, the eight stations will provide 8,617 MW of generating capacity. Cascades of hydropower stations have also been built in Karelia, near the Kola Peninsula in the north, and in the mountainous region of the Caucasus. The Sevan-Razdan Cascade in Armenia consists of six diversion-type power plants, with tunnels and penstocks bringing the water down to the generating stations.

Because many of the western rivers are flanked by valuable urban, industrial, or agricultural land that would be flooded by additional hydropower reservoirs, little future expansion is likely, compared to that planned in other parts of the country. Consequently, in 1985 only 40 percent of total hydroelectric power production is to be generated in the European USSR including the Urals, a drop from 54 percent in 1970.

Soviet Central Asia

Dams are especially important in the dry climate of Central Asia. Besides producing power for industrial development, they also provide water to irrigate the cottonfields and orchards.

In the Kirghiz and Tajik Republics several high dams have been built in difficult mountainous terrain; on the Vakhsh River in Tajikistan, the 2,700-MW Nurek power station is complete, and construction is under way on the 3,600-MW Rogun station; on the Naryn River in Kirgizia four hydroelectric stations are operating, the largest being the 1,200-MW Toktogul station. The total capacity of the hydroelectric power stations now under construction in the mountains of Central Asia will exceed 9,000 MW if all planned construction is completed.

Siberia and the Soviet Far East

The Siberian regions contain two-thirds of the total USSR hydropower potential, but little of it had been tapped until recently. In the past 20 years, however, massive construction projects in this remote, environmentally inhospitable area have led to steady growth in hydropower output.

The Angara-Yenisey basin in eastern Siberia alone contains one-fourth of the country's total hydroelectric resources, capable of producing more than 300 billion kWh of electricity annually. When completed in 1966, the 4,500-MW Bratsk station on the Angara River was the largest hydropower station in the world. Later, in 1971, the 6,000-MW Krasnoyarsk station on the Yenisey River achieved this distinction. An even larger hydroelectric power station, the Sayan-Shushenskoye Hydropower Station on the upper Yenisey River, with 6,400 MW, is to be completed in the mid-1980s. With the completion of other stations under construction or planned, the total capacity of the Angara-Yenisey Cascade could reach 46,700 MW by the end of the century.

Several large hydropower stations built on the Zeya and Bureya Rivers in the Soviet Far East are to provide power for new industry in the area, as well as for the eastern sector of the new Baikal-Amur Mainline (BAM) railroad.

In the far northern regions the Soviets have built hydropower plants in the permafrost zone, where special construction techniques are required because of the unique characteristics of the ground surface and the rigors of the environment. The first plant in this region was built on the Vilyuy River in the Yakut ASSR, where winter temperatures drop to −60 degrees Celsius. A 900-MW hydropower plant is being built in the far northeast on the Kolyma River. It will greatly increase the power available in Magadan Oblast, where more than 1,000 scattered diesel generating stations now provide most of the power.

Construction of 1,325-MW Inguri Hydropower Dam across Inguri River in the Caucasus Mountains, Georgian SSR.

Nuclear Power

In 1954 the Soviet Union became the first country to use nuclear power to generate electricity for commercial purposes. The Soviets were subsequently slow to capitalize on their strong start and made little progress until the mid-1970s. Since then, however, the pace of nuclear development has picked up rapidly despite the chronic construction delays that plague virtually all Soviet projects. Based on the aggressive program Moscow now has on the books to expand existing plants and add new ones, most informed observers expect that strong growth should continue throughout this decade and into the early 1990s, even with continuing construction bottlenecks.

Untroubled by antinuclear protests and increasingly supported by a sizable industry dedicated to the manufacture of nuclear reactor components, the Soviets now have one of the most active nuclear power construction programs in the world. The 11th Five-Year Plan (1981-85) projected the addition of 24,000 to 25,000 megawatts of nuclear capacity and a production of 220 billion kWh of electricity in 1985. At the beginning of 1984, the USSR had 12 nuclear power stations with one or more operating reactors, combining for a total electrical generating capacity of 20,168 MW, and additional reactors were still under construction at six of these operating stations. Electricity generated at these stations accounted for 8 percent of total Soviet electricity output in 1983. Additionally, 11 new nuclear power stations and two district heat stations were under construction.

Except for Bilibino in northeastern Siberia, and the noncommercial plant at Shevchenko in Kazakhstan, the Soviet Union's installed and

Nuclear Power Stations

Power stations
Operational
(capacity in MW)

● 3,000 and above
● 1,500 to 3,000
• Less than 1,500

○ Under construction

Note: Figures indicate number of reactors.
Refer to page 67 for listing.

Scale 1:22,000,000

Exterior view of 2,455-MW Novovoronezhskiy Atomic Power Station.

planned nuclear power capacity is concentrated in the European USSR. Soviet policy for locating nuclear power plants is aimed at concentrating facilities in the country's most heavily populated and industrialized regions, which are characterized by a deficiency of fossil fuels and other forms of power relative to more remote and less populated regions of the country.

All nuclear power stations in the Soviet Union, and most of the existing and planned stations in the neighboring CEMA countries, are built around Soviet-designed reactors that use uranium fuel slightly enriched in the isotope uranium-235 (U-235). The Soviets have designed two types of power reactors: the pressurized water reactor (PWR) and the graphite-moderated pressure-tube (boiling water) reactor (GMPTR). The pressurized water reactor, designated VVER, comes in two main models, the VVER-440, a 440-megawatt (electrical) model, and the VVER-1000, a 1,000-megawatt (electrical) model. Two smaller prototypes or early demonstration models, the VVER-210 and the VVER-365, are also in operation. The graphite reactors are designated as RBMK. Of these, the RBMK-1000 model is the largest operational; however, the RBMK-1500—a 1,500-megawatt model—started up in late 1983 at Ignalina, Lithuania.

The Soviets are also continuing development of a third type—a liquid-metal, fast-breeder reactor (LMFBR). Only two major Soviet breeder reactors are currently in operation: a 350-megawatt prototype at Shevchenko, designated BN-350 and a 600-megawatt prototype at Beloyarskiy, designated BN-600. Several small, research fast breeder reactors are also in use.

In addition to continuing emphasis on the expansion of domestic nuclear power generation, the USSR is committed to a joint venture with its CEMA partners in Europe to develop a unified nuclear power program. A total of 11 Soviet-designed, 440-megawatt, pressurized water reactors are already in operation in CEMA-member states, and many more are planned. A nuclear power station with two VVER-440s is currently operating in Finland. Construction has also begun on a Soviet-designed nuclear power station in Cuba.

Reactor being readied for startup at South Ukraine Nuclear Power Station.

To meet its goals for domestic nuclear power growth and, at the same time, honor its commitments to CEMA partners, the Soviet Union is continuing to increase its capacity for manufacturing nuclear reactors, components, and equipment. The recently expanded Izhorskiy Heavy Equipment Plant at Kolpino near Leningrad and the newly constructed Volgodonsk Heavy Machine Plant, known as Atommash, are two of the largest nuclear component fabrication plants in the world. The location of the much-publicized Atommash plant along the Don River allows shipment of large reactor units by barge to sites throughout European USSR. Czechoslovakia, using components manufactured there and by other CEMA countries, assembles the Soviet-designed VVER-440 and has plans to produce the VVER-1000 reactors.

District Heat Systems

The Soviets are constructing several nuclear stations whose function is to produce heat or both heat and electricity for homes and industries at nearby towns and cities. Two types of these facilities are currently under construction: the first type, designated AST, is a boiling water reactor. Through a three-loop thermal exchange process, heat generated by the reactor is transported into the town's district heating system. The Soviets are building stations of this type, each consisting of two reactors of 500 MW (thermal) at Gor'kiy and Voronezh. A second type, designated ATETs, is a modification of the existing VVER-1000 reactor. In this system, a portion of the steam, which is normally used to produce electricity in the turbines, is diverted and used as a heat source for the district heating system. Because of the high calorific content of the steam, it is possible to transmit heat 30 to 40 kilometers. Construction of stations of this second type has been started at Odessa and Minsk, and the Soviets have announced plans to construct others at Khar'kov and Volgograd.

Interior of the fourth RBMK-1000 power unit at the Leningrad Nuclear Power Station.

Power Transmission

The USSR's unified power transmission system covers more area than any other power transmission system in the world. In 1983, 852,000 kilometers of high-voltage transmission lines interconnected more than 90 percent of the country's generating capacity. The basic units of the USSR's electricity transmission system are the 95 regional power networks called energos. Formed of 110- and 220-kV AC transmission lines, each network supplies power to a single administrative region (oblast, kray) or industrial region. Over the years most of these regional networks have been linked by 220-kV and 500-kV lines to form 11 consolidated regional power systems (OES).

A merger of the regional systems began in the mid-1950s and is complete except for the independently operated consolidated systems of Central Asia and the Far East. These two isolated power systems are to be connected to the national network—known as the Unified Power System of the Soviet Union (USSR YeES)—by the end of the 12th Five-Year Plan (1986-90). The USSR YeES is also linked to the power systems of many neighboring countries: CEMA countries, Finland, Norway, and Turkey.

The integration of the OES into the USSR YeES has increased the flexibility of Soviet power supply; power can now be transferred between the linked systems, albeit at present only in small amounts. For example, only a 500-MW load can be transmitted from Siberia to Kazakhstan. The Soviets hope, however, eventually to be able to transmit large blocks of electricity—40 billion kWh and more—from the eastern regions, where energy resources are cheap and plentiful, to the power-hungry, but resource-poor European USSR. The transmission of so much power over so long a distance is unprecedented, in fact infeasible, until ultrahigh-voltage (UHV) power transmission is perfected.

In general, the higher the voltage a transmission line can accept, the greater its capacity and efficiency and the farther it may be extended. Higher voltage transmission permits exploitation of hydropower resources far from

More than 800,000 kilometers of high-voltage transmission lines interconnect more than 90 percent of Soviet generating capacity.

A helicopter is used to erect 500-kV AC transmission towers in the Caucasus Mountains.

Selected Types of Towers for Extra-High (EHV) and Ultrahigh-Voltage (UHV) Transmission

750-kV AC   800-kV DC   1,150-kV AC   1,500-kV DC

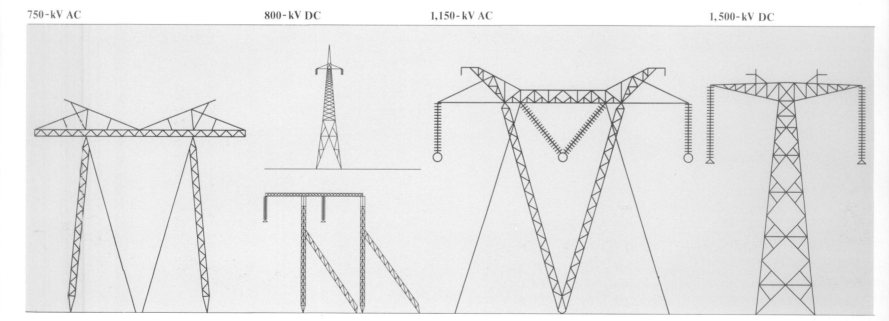

consuming centers and of deposits of brown coal whose calorific value is too low to justify shipping it long distances. Spurred by such considerations, the Soviet Union has become a world leader in the development of UHV power transmission technology.

In the realm of UHV power transmission, Soviet engineers are proceeding on two fronts. They are continuing to develop UHV AC transmission but are also working on UHV DC transmission.

The USSR has announced that an experimental 1,150-kV AC powerline under construction in northern Kazakhstan will originate at the Ekibastuz-1 GRES and terminate at Chelyabinsk in the Urals. The first 600-km segment to Kokchetav was to be energized at 500 kV in late 1984. A 600-km eastward extension from the Ekibastuz-1 GRES to Barnaul in Siberia, and later to Novokuznetsk, is also under construction. Not only will the line greatly strengthen the tie between the Unified Power Systems of Siberia and north Kazakhstan, it will also tie in the major industrial cities in the Urals, to which it will carry power generated by the many new thermal power plants now in various phases of planning and construction in the Kansk-Achinsk and Ekibastuz coal basins.

Ultra-high-voltage DC transmission can move power over very long distances with lower line losses than AC transmission. Soviet development of DC transmission began in 1956 with the construction of an experimental 800-kV DC line between the Donets basin in the Ukraine and the Volgograd Hydropower Station some 473 kilometers away; it began operating in 1962. This line, which carries 750 MW, linked the OES of the Center and the South regions. The experience gleaned from this 800-kV DC line led the Soviets to begin construction in early 1980 of a 1,500-kV DC line from Ekibastuz to Tambov, south of Moscow, a distance of 2,400 kilometers. But work on this line ceased in 1981 when the entire UHV effort shifted to the 1,150-kV AC system.

Electrification of rural areas in the USSR has grown rapidly in the last two decades as a result of the vast expansion of the countrywide power transmission capacity and the consolidation and centralization of local power generation. In the early 1960s small local power stations supplied nearly 50 percent of the power used in the countryside. Since then most of these stations have been dismantled, and state power grids now supply most of the electricity consumed in rural areas. To carry the increased amount of centrally produced power, the rural transmission network has quadrupled in length since 1960. More than 92 percent of this network consists of small distribution lines of 20 kV or less; the remainder are 35-kV, 110-kV, and 220-kV main lines.

The rapid growth in rural electric power was designed to improve the efficiency of agriculture through mechanization and to raise the standard of living in the countryside, where powerlines now reach most farms.

Workmen installing 1,150-kV AC transmission lines between Kazakhstan and the Urals.

Unified Power System

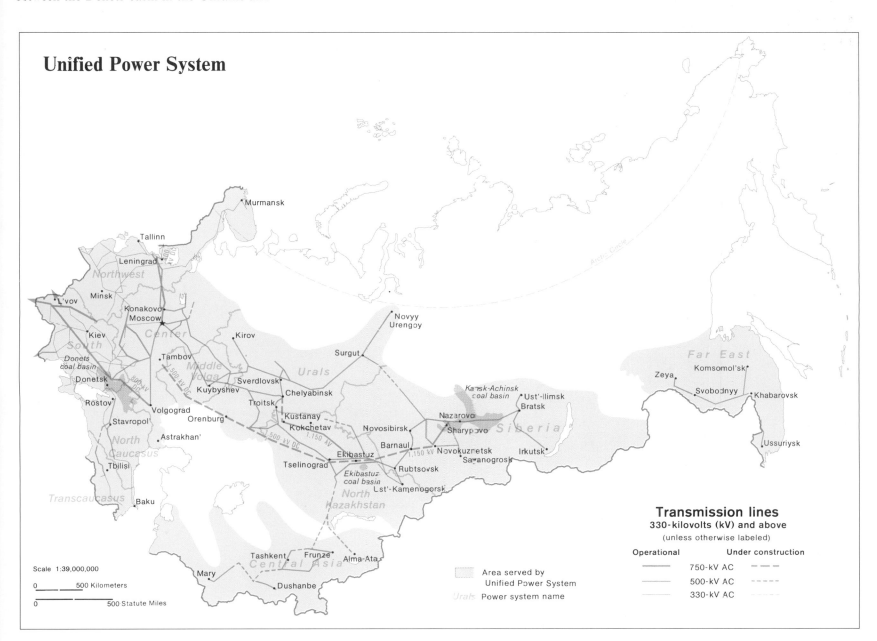

Transmission lines
330-kilovolts (kV) and above
(unless otherwise labeled)

Operational	Under construction
750-kV AC	
500-kV AC	
330-kV AC	

Area served by Unified Power System

Urals Power system name

Scale 1:39,000,000

0 ——— 500 Kilometers

0 ——— 500 Statute Miles

Power Plants and Transmission Lines

Svalbard (Norway)

Neth.

West Germany

East Germany

Czech.

Hun.

Poland

Romania

Turkey

Iraq

Iran

Afghanistan

Pakistan

India

China

Norway

Sweden

Finland

Denmark

Baltic Sea

Barents Sea

Kara Sea

Black Sea

Caspian Sea

Aral Sea

Lake Balkhash

Arctic Circle

Kirkenes
Nikel' 154-kV
Murmansk
Kirovsk
Varzino
Iokanga

Kaliningrad
Liepāja Ventspils
Klaipēda
Pärnu
Haapsalu
Tallinn
Riga
Valmiera
Imatra
Slantsy
Pskov
Leningrad
Lodeynoye Pole
Petrozavodsk
Severodvinsk
Arkhangel'sk
Segezha
Vytegra
Razgort
Pechora
Usinsk Inta
Vorkuta
Ukhta

Ketrzyn
Białystok
Brest
Kovel' Pinsk
Vilnius
Minsk Polotsk
Novgorod
Tikhvin
Bologoye
Nelidovo
Cherepovets
Vologda
Velikiy Ustyug
Kotlas
Mikun'
Luza
Skytyvkar
Kholmogory

Kaišiadorys
L'vov Lutsk Sarny
Rovno
Chernovtsy
Vinnitsa
Bel'tsy
Ungeny
Gayvoron
Izmail
Odessa
Kherson
Yevpatoriya
Sevastopol'
Yalta
Simferopol'
Kerch'

Vitebsk
Mogilev
Smolensk Rzhev
Safonovo
Kalinin
Konakovo
Gomel'
Bryansk
Kaluga
Moscow
Zagorsk
Yaroslavl'
Kostroma
Kineshma
Kiev
Nezhin
Konotop
Zheleznogorsk
Orël
Kursk
Sumy
Khar'kov
Gubkin
Lipetsk
Voronezh
Michurinsk
Georgiu-Dezh
Tambov
Ruzayevka
Penza
Dnepropetrovsk
Novonikolayevskiy
Donetsk
Uglegorsk
Rostov
Morozovsk
Sal'sk
Ryazan'
Sasovo
Arzamas
Vladimir
Gor'kiy
Cheboksary
Kazan'
Kotel'nich
Kirov
Rudnichnyy
Gayny
Krasnovishersk
Novyy Urengoy Urengoy
Nizhnevartovsk
Surgut

Zamość
Rzeszów
Mukachevo
Bál Mare
Konotop

Novorossiysk
Krasnodar
Tikhoretsk
Maykop
Sochi
Sukhumi
Hopa
Batumi
Stavropol'
Pyatigorsk
Budennovsk
Mozdok
Ordzhonikidze
Groznyy
Tbilisi
Leninakan
Lagodekhi
Yerevan
Nakhichevan'
Agdam
Khachmas
Kyurdamir
Yeraliyev
Baku
Astara
Makhachkala
Shevchenko
Uzen'
Novyy Uzen'
Beyneu
Astrakhan'
Volgograd
Kamyshin
Aleksandrov Gay
Elista
Kalmykovo
Inderborskiy
Ural'sk
Gur'yev
Dossor
Kul'sary
Emba
Saratov
Syzran'
Kuybyshev
Kinel'
Bugul'ma
Zainsk
Sterlitamak
Orenburg
Perm'
Votkinsk
Chusovoy
Serov
Ufa
Sverdlovsk
Tavda
Zlatoust
Chelyabinsk
Tyumen'
Tobol'sk
Magnitogorsk
Troitsk
Kurgan
Makushino
Ishim
Vikulovo
Tara
Orsk
Dzhetygara
Kustanay
Lisakovsk
Aktyubinsk
Khromtau
Karabutak
Turgay
Chelkar
Amangel'dy
Tselinograd
Ekibastuz
Pavlodar
Baykonur
Dzhezkazgan
Karaganda
Karazhal
Yegindybulak
Karagayly
Balkhash
Sary-Ozek
Sayak
Bakanas
Dzhansugurov
Taldy-Kurgan
Panfilov
Alma-Ata
Frunze
Rybach'ye
Chayek
Naryn
Przheval'sk
Osh
Andizhan
Namangan
Tashkent
Dzhambul
Chimkent
Kentau
Zhanatas
Arys'
Talas
Turkestan
Kzyl-Orda
Chiili
Aral'sk
Leninsk (Tyuratam)
Kungrad
Nukus
Urgench
Tashauz
Kizyl-Arvat
Ashkhabad
Nebit-Dag
Krasnovodsk
Cheleken
Kizyl-Arvat
Gazli
Zarafshan
Navoi
Bukhara
Chardzhou
Karshi
Guzar
Kerki
Tedzhen
Mary
Takhta-Bazar
Kushka
Denau
Tursunzade
Dushanbe
Nurek
Kalai-Khumb
Kolkhozabad
Kulyab
Samarkand
Leninabad
Kokand

Omsk
Tatarsk
Novosibirsk
Chulym
Tomsk
Sharypovo
Kochki
Suzun
Karasuk
Barnaul
Biysk
Rubtsovsk
Semipalatinsk
Gorno-Altaysk
Ust'-Kamenogorsk
Leninogorsk
Zyryanovsk
Ak-Dovu
Abaz
Novokuznetsk
Sergeyevka
Kokchetav
Aysarinskoye
Makinsk
Aksu
Yesil'
Tatarka
Petropavlovsk

Scale 1:17,000,000

0 ——————— 500 Kilometers

0 ——————— 500 Statute Miles

Power plants

■ Operational   □ Under construction

Capacity in megawatts (MW)

	100–300	301–1,000	Over 1,000
Thermal			
Hydro			
Nuclear			

Transmission lines

—— Operational   - - - Under construction

Capacity in kilovolts (kV) AC *

110   220   330   500

* Unless otherwise labeled

*Note: All power plants with capacities greater than 1,000 MW and transmission
lines with 220 kV or greater are included. Only selected power plants and
transmission lines with lesser capacities are shown.*

57

Power for Remote Areas

Economic activity in the Soviet Union is concentrated mainly in the European part of the country and along narrow bands of relatively well-developed territory flanking major transportation routes such as the Trans-Siberian Railroad. These areas comprise far less than half of the total Soviet landmass. Enormous areas in the European north, in Siberia and the Soviet Far East, and in Kazakhstan and Soviet Central Asia are lightly populated and unserved by rail or powerline, hence undeveloped, although they contain vast quantities of natural resources needed for continued Soviet economic growth. From desert to steppe to taiga to tundra,

exploitation of these resources requires electric power. Transmission lines have been extended from core areas to some major natural resource processing centers, but often this is not feasible—usually because of the sheer distance involved—and the needed power must be generated locally. Only 3 percent of all power produced in the country is generated in areas beyond the reach of regional power grids, but an estimated 5 million Soviet citizens depend on it.

When the demand justifies it, large power plants are built in isolated areas. Noril'sk, for example, with its population of 183,000 and its important copper, nickel, and platinum mining industries, is supported by three sizable power plants: two are thermal plants with a combined capacity of 825 MW fueled by natural gas from the

Messoyakha field and the other is the nearby 441-MW Khantayka Hydropower Plant at Snezhnogorsk. The city of Yakutsk (population 175,000) in the heart of the Soviet Far East has a 165-MW power plant fueled from nearby gasfields. The 648-MW Vilyuy Hydroelectric Power Station at Chernyshevskiy supplies power to diamond-mining areas in the north and Mirnyy and Lensk (a Lena River port) in the south.

For isolated and remote areas of the Soviet Union where power requirements are small, electric power is generated by diesel-powered generators (DES) and to a lesser extent by gas-turbine generators (GTU). The Soviets have developed a full line of these, ranging from small units such as a 20-kV diesel generator made at the Kursk Mobile Unit plant for use by

Vilyuy Hydroelectric Power Station in Eastern Siberia's Yakut ASSR is one of the northernmost in the USSR.

shepherds, to 12-MW units that can be grouped to supply power to entire towns. However, the current emphasis is to replace, where possible, these inefficient, relatively expensive portable generators with the more efficient transmission networks centered on large regional power plants.

Where conditions permit, power stations may be mounted on trucks, trains, or ships. Mobile generating units mounted on railway cars have been used for many industrial construction projects in remote areas. A power train supported the construction of the Bratsk Hydropower Station, for example. A 24-MW power train incor-

porating two diesel-fueled gas-turbine generators was used at tunnel construction sites on the Baikal-Amur Mainline (BAM) railroad. An automated 500-kW diesel station mounted in a truck-drawn van was developed particularly for use by the builders of the BAM.

The responsibility for development and production of small, transportable power plants was centralized in 1947 with the formation of the State All-Union Production Trust for Mobile Power Plants. Besides development and production, the Trust is also responsible for maintenance and repair. The Trust is mandated to develop generating units that are even more

economical, efficient, mobile, and rugged; some current models can operate at temperatures as high as 45 degrees and as low as −60 degrees Celsius.

During the 1970s, five floating gas-turbine (GTU) power stations, designated Severnoye Siyaniye (Northern Lights), were built at the Tyumen' Shipyard to seagoing specifications. These ship stations lack their own propulsion systems and have to be towed to the remote sites where they are used to generate electricity for industries, construction sites, mining, and petroleum exploitation. Each of the first three power ships had two 10-MW oil-fueled gas-turbine generators, while the fourth and fifth ships were equipped with two 12-MW gas-fueled generators. Subsequent power ships in this series are to have 48-MW generating capacities.

The development of electric power in the mining area (gold and other heavy metals) near the mouth of the Kolyma River illustrates the various ways in which power may be supplied to an isolated place. That very remote region on the Arctic Ocean in the Soviet Far East is served only by air and by the seasonal Soviet Northern Sea Route; neither roads nor rails connect it with other parts of the country, and the nearest regional power grid is more than 2,000 kilometers away. To supply power for the expansion of gold mining, a small, coal-fired thermal power

plant at the port of Pevek was initially augmented by some diesel generators and a power train (delivered by ship). Then in 1970 Severnoye Siyaniye-1 arrived at the port of Zelenyy Mys on the lower Kolyma River. The floating power station provided more power for mining but also supported construction of the 48-MW nuclear TETs at Bilibino, which went into operation in 1973.

To free power consumers in remote areas from dependence on fuel supply, alternative energy sources are receiving attention. A 2-kW wind-driven power unit that can be carried by packhorse has been developed for prospectors, shepherds, and mountain farmers. Solar power units have also been developed for such users. A

modular nuclear power station specifically designed for use in remote areas is probably now in the testing stage. Its 15-ton modules are air transportable. Its reactor, which supplies steam to a 1.5-MW turbine generator, can operate five years on a single fueling of slightly enriched uranium.

The Severnoye Siyaniye (Northern Lights) floating power station is one of five built at the Tyumen' Shipyard.

Neryungri Thermal Power Plant in the Yakut ASSR is being fueled by Neryungri coal.

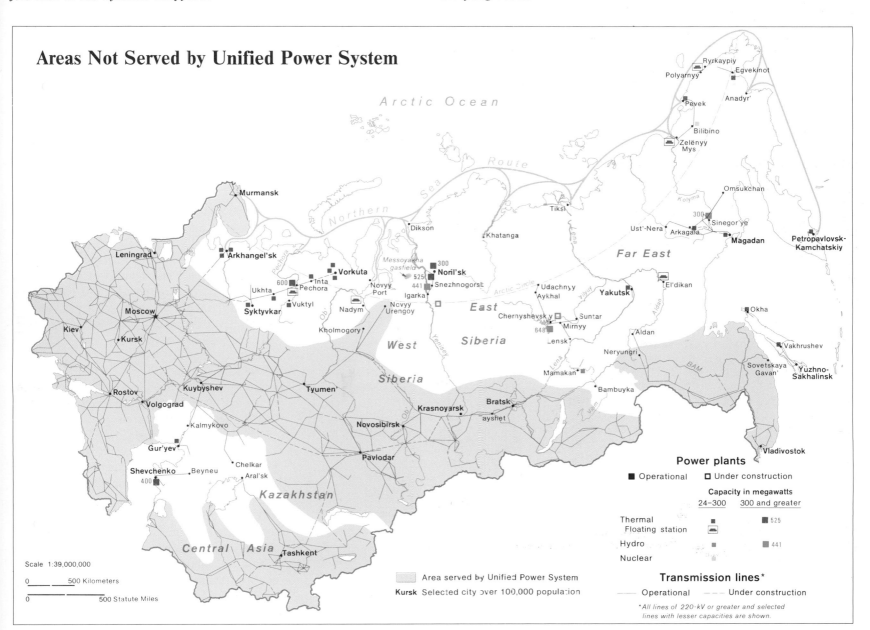

Areas Not Served by Unified Power System

Alternative Energy Sources and Technologies

Spurred by the spiraling costs of fuel production and transport, as well as the depletion of easily accessible fuel reserves, the Soviet Union is devoting increased attention to the exploitation of alternative energy sources and advanced energy technologies. Energy planners have long viewed the conversion of Siberian brown coal into synfuel derivatives as a major potential source of supplemental fuel. Various other methods of obtaining heat, electricity, and mechanical power from solar, wind, tidal, and

geothermal energy are under study, as are vehicular engines that can burn liquefied gas, hydrogen, or alcohol. Magnetohydrodynamic (MHD) devices, which would greatly improve the fuel efficiency of conventional thermal power plants, are in the pilot-plant stage of development. Nuclear fusion is also under investigation as a potential source of a virtually limitless supply of electricity.

The Soviets, nonetheless, continue to view most alternative energy sources as too speculative and costly to justify major development efforts. Funding in these areas is still sufficient only for limited and selected technological investigation, construction of prototype equipment and pilot plants, and gradual introduction of small-scale applications. Even if given a strong push now, none of these energy sources would probably contribute significantly to the Soviet energy balance before the end of the century.

USSR: Alternative and Advanced Energy Applications—A Speculative Sampler

Time Frame	Application	Energy Source	Device
Current to near term (0 to 10 years)	Building and greenhouse heating, water heating, crop drying	Low-temperature geothermal heat, solar radiation	Heat exchangers, absorption devices
	Water pumping	Low-velocity wind	Windmills
		Solar radiation	Solar steam engines
	Cooking	Solar radiation	Solar cookstoves
	Water desalination	Solar radiation	Solar evaporators
	Smelting	Solar radiation	Solar furnaces
	Electricity (*KW*)	Solar radiation	Photovoltaic devices
	Electricity (*MW*)	Medium-temperature geothermal heat, solar radiation	Heat exchangers, solar concentrators driving binary-cycle generators
		High-velocity wind	Wind turbine generators
Medium term (10 to 20 years)	Vehicular propulsion	Hydrogen, LNG, alcohol	New types of engines
	Electricity (*hundreds of MW*) (feasibility to be demonstrated)	Fossil fuels, especially coal	Magnetohydrodynamic (MHD) generators
		High-temperature geothermal heat, solar radiation	Heat exchangers, solar concentrators driving steam turbines
Long term (beyond 20 years)	Electricity (*hundreds of MW*) (feasibility to be demonstrated)	Deuterium (isotope of hydrogen obtained from water)	Thermonuclear fusion reactors driving steam turbines
		Ocean tides	Hydroelectric generators

Coal-Based Synfuels

The large and well-known disparities between the USSR's eastern energy resources and the fuel requirements for industrial development of the European USSR have caused the Soviets to focus increased attention on the brown coal (lignite) reserves of Siberia. Soviet scientists, engineers, and economists have devoted particular attention over the past 10 to 15 years to developing an economical technique to convert the brown coal reserves of Central Siberia's Kansk-Achinsk basin into better quality and more easily transportable liquid and solid fuels.

Kansk-Achinsk brown coal is an attractive source of energy for the European USSR if processing and transportation methods can be developed. This coal is readily extracted through low-cost, open-pit mining; however, its high

moisture content (35 percent), low-heating value (3,300 kilocalories per kilogram), and variable physical and chemical characteristics render its direct shipment to power plants in European USSR highly uneconomical. Kansk-Achinsk brown coal also subject to spontaneous combustion in storage and transit and tends to freeze together in cold weather, making it difficult to handle.

Although commercial production of coal-derived fuels is difficult to justify economically, the Soviets still regard coal conversion as a promising potential means of exploiting their vast Central Siberian brown coal reserves. This is evidenced by Moscow's recent appointment of a coordinator for synfuels development and the construction of a demonstration facility for the pyrolysis of coal and a pilot plant for direct liquefaction.

In 1976 the Soviets began construction of a high-speed pyrolysis demonstration plant at Krasnoyarsk in the Kansk-Achinsk basin. The stated objective of this plant is to extract semi-coke (similar to charcoal), synthetic oil, and hydrocarbon gases from lignite.

Reportedly, the completion of the Krasnoyarsk demonstration plant has been delayed, and the Soviets are now showing increased interest in a number of other synfuel technologies. Most recently the Soviets announced construction of two developmental coal liquefaction facilities, one near the Belkovskaya lignite mine in the Moscow coal basin and a second at the Berezovskoye mine in the Kansk-Achinsk basin. The Belkovskaya pilot plant—based on the Soviet version of World War II, German standard direct liquefaction coal hydrogenation technology—is designed to produce 18 barrels of oil per day; the Berezovskoye pilot plant is reportedly designed for about 550 barrels per day. The Soviets are also seeking access to additional Western coal-conversion technology.

In the 1930s the USSR became the first country in the world to develop a successful program for converting underground coal into gas. Since then, however, their progress on underground coal gasification has been slow. Only two of the half-dozen pilot plants operating in the early 1960s remain in use. The much-publicized pilot underground coal gasification plant near Angren, southeast of Tashkent, and another plant at Yuzhno-Abinsk have yet to operate at an economical level. In spite of the apparent decline of interest in underground coal gasification, the Soviets are continuing to study economic ways to apply this and other techniques to exploit deep-lying coal deposits.

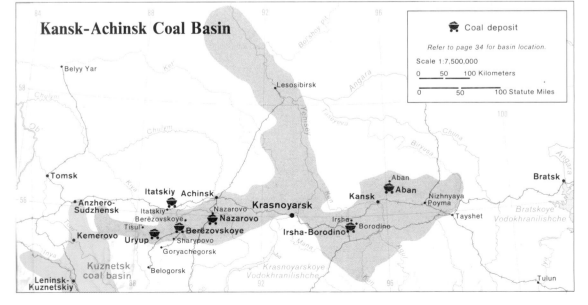

Kansk-Achinsk Coal Basin

♦ Coal deposit

Refer to page 34 for basin location.

Scale 1:7,500,000

0   50   100 Kilometers

0   50   100 Statute Miles

Solar Energy

The USSR is developing solar energy for a wide variety of small-scale uses, such as heating and desalinating water, heating and cooling buildings, cooking food, and powering small steam engines, water pumps, and electric generators to serve consumers scattered throughout rural areas in the southern USSR. In these applications, the sun's radiant energy is used to heat water or air.

In addition, the Soviets are working on the conversion of solar energy to electricity using the photovoltaic effect, in which an electric current is generated between two tightly joined, dissimilar materials when they are exposed to light. Applying research that produced power cells for spacecraft, the Soviets are also developing small photovoltaic devices for more mundane uses—for example, to prevent corrosion of pipelines and to power navigation beacons. Reportedly, their largest photovoltaic device is a 500-watt motor.

Solar research is coordinated by the State Committee for Science and Technology and by the USSR Academy of Sciences. Research and testing are done primarily in institutes in the areas of the USSR south of the 50 degrees N latitude, where the technologies will be most used.

In 1979, at Bikrova, a suburb of Ashkhabad in Soviet Central Asia, the Turkmen SSR Academy of Sciences created the Solar Energy Institute (SOLNTSE), which is said to be the first in the country. A research and production corporation for solar energy equipment, SOLNTSE, is to develop devices to meet small-scale energy needs in desert areas.

The Uzbek SSR is the only republic reported to have officially directed that solar equipment be installed in some public buildings. In 1980 the Uzbek city of Chirchik claimed to have the nation's first residential building using solar energy to supply its hot water and heat. A small factory at Bukhara in the republic is the only known industrial producer of solar equipment in the USSR.

Transforming solar energy into thermal and electric power is studied by workers at the Uzbek SSR Academy of Sciences.

A solar energy experiment to grow chlorella (a type of alga), near Ashkhabad, Turkmen SSR.

Solar power station at Bikrova, Turkmen SSR.

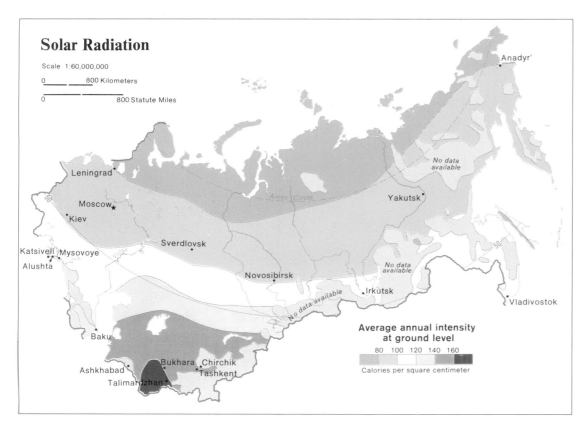

Solar Radiation

Scale 1:60,000,000

0 —— 800 Kilometers

0 —— 800 Statute Miles

Anadyr'

No data available

Leningrad
Moscow
Kiev
Sverdlovsk
Katsiveli Mysovoye
Alushta
Novosibirsk
Yakutsk
Irkutsk
No data available
Vladivostok
Baku
Bukhara Chirchik
Ashkhabad Tashkent
Talimardzhan

Average annual intensity at ground level

80 100 120 140 160

Calories per square centimeter

Engineers adjust solar thermoelectric generator at Turkmen Academy of Sciences research center.

In the European USSR the Ukrainian Academy of Sciences is the primary agency for solar energy development. Several of its institutes are working on solar heating and cooling systems, and a research and testing center for such systems has been established at the Crimean resort city of Alushta on the Black Sea. Cooperating in this work are the USSR State Committee for Civil Construction and Architecture and the Solar Power Engineering Laboratory of the Krzhizhanovskiy Power Engineering Institute (ENIN) in Moscow. And, continuing the long-standing Soviet use of solar furnaces to study high-temperature processes, the Ukrainian Academy has also established a solar furnace facility at Katsiveli in the Crimea to produce pure metal alloys.

As for the large-scale production of solar electric power, the Soviets are still largely in the conceptual and planning stage. They claim to have designed a practical solar boiler and hope to complete a 5-MW solar power test facility by 1986 at Mysovoye, near Lenino in the Crimea. This facility is to have 1,600 heliostats—movable mirrors—each 5 meters square. The heliostats will focus the sun's rays on a boiler atop a tower 100 meters high to produce steam to drive an electric power generator.

A much larger (300-MW) solar power station has been designed for the same site, but its cost will make it economically uncompetitive with conventional power plants for a very long time. Soviet energy planners estimate that by century's end large solar power plants will come closest to being competitive in the Crimea and in the lower Volga region but will still not match costs in conventional plants. In the meantime, the Krzhizhanovskiy Institute has worked out an engineering concept that combines solar energy with a conventional fuel such as gas. The initial stage of such a project might involve 300 MW, using a 100-MW solar unit when solar energy is available and a 200-MW, gas-burning unit the rest of the time. Talimardzhan in the Uzbek SSR has been selected as a tentative site for the project.

Wind Energy

Windpower has long been extensively exploited on farms in the USSR. Indeed, the Soviets claim that 250,000 windmills were in use in the rural areas of prerevolutionary Russia. Today, tens of thousands of homemade windmills are still used in the steppe regions, mainly to pump water. In the arid southern portions of the country and the remote regions of the north, windmills serve as alternative or auxiliary sources of mechanical and electrical power in areas beyond the reach of regional power grids.

Despite widespread recognition of the practical utility of the windmill, uncoordinated research on windpowered devices in laboratories of the agricultural, aeronautical, and electrical equipment ministries has produced few significant technical advances to date. One flurry of governmental interest just after World War II resulted in the production of some 40,000 wind engines, which were used with great effectiveness on farms. By the early 1970s, however, fewer than 9,000 of these were still in operation. Then in 1975 a national corporation named Tsiklon (cyclone) was created under the Ministry of Land Reclamation and Water Resources; its mission is to develop and introduce windpowered devices into the Soviet economy. Although the market for such items has been estimated to be at least 150,000 units, the 1976-80 Five-Year Plan called for an output of only 10,000 units, and by 1980 only 4,500 had been produced.

Most Soviet windpowered devices, whether of the propeller or vertical axis type, are small (15 to 20 kW). A 100-kW wind engine, however, was installed near Yalta in 1931; a 12-element, 400-kW auxiliary power plant was built in Kazakhstan in the 1950s; and, more recently, a 10-element, 400-kW power unit has been installed in Arkhangel'sk Oblast.

Reportedly, Tsiklon engineers have developed a series of windpowered, electricity-generating systems with capacities ranging from 1 to 100 kW. Series production of a 6-kW windpowered generator is under way, and other units with capacities up to 100 kW are in the test stage. The largest units are designed to supply power to small villages on the steppes of Kazakhstan and in the Far North, regions where sustained winds of 6 to 10 meters per second are common. The feasibility of developing still more powerful units with output capacities of 1 to 5 MW is being studied.

Because wind is only an intermittent energy source, windpowered generators must be integrated with other forms of generating equipment, such as diesel generators. Tsiklon is beginning to design such packages, but none is yet in serial production.

Tsiklon operates development and test facilities at Istra, near Moscow, and at Novorossiysk, a new national test center in the mountains on the Black Sea coast. The Novorossiysk area was chosen because of the frequent occurrence of a very strong local wind known as *bora*. Tsiklon-developed windpower pumps are also being tested by a wind engineering laboratory at the Kishinev Polytechnic Institute in Moldavia.

Tidal Power

France, China, and the Soviet Union are the only nations now generating electricity from ocean tides. In 1968, with the help of French technology, the Soviets completed a 400-kW pilot tidal power station at Guba Kislaya on the Barents Sea, which feeds into the Kola electric grid. Although the amount of power generated by this initial effort is meager, Soviet engineers, operating under the auspices of the Ministry of Power and Electrification, believe that the potential of tides as a source of energy is great.

No additional construction has been commissioned, but some 20 sites have been identified where exploitation of tidal energy may be feasible, if not yet economically practicable. A number of the proposed installations are huge, such as a 10,000-MW tidal power station in Mezenskaya Guba that would involve building a dam 96 kilometers long. Even this project—which if constructed would be the world's largest and most expensive hydropower installation—would be dwarfed by the most ambitious of these schemes, a 100,000-MW tidal power station in Penzhinskaya Guba. By comparison, a relatively modest 300-MW tidal power station in Lumbovskiy Zaliv would contain 24 encapsulated hydrogenerators in two dams totaling 2.8 kilometers in length, making it a rather expensive way to obtain 300 MW of capacity. It is doubtful that the Soviets will build any major tidal power stations soon.

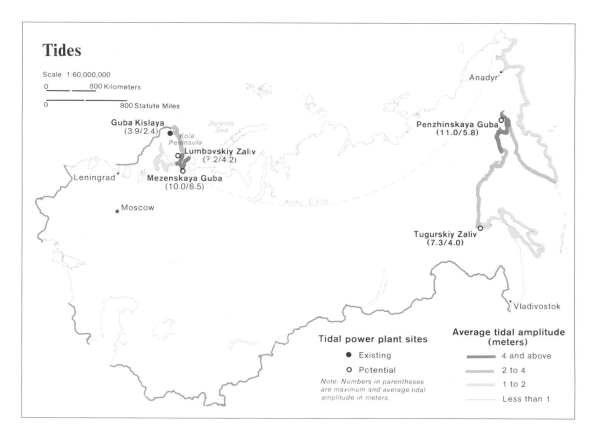

Kislaya Guba tidal power station on the Kola Peninsula.

Another view of the Kislaya Guba tidal power station.

Geothermal Energy

Even though the Soviet Union may have the largest undeveloped geothermal resources in the world, its geothermal research and development program lags similar programs in the United States, Japan, New Zealand, and Italy. According to some current Soviet estimates, hot rock and magma—from which heat energy above 100 degrees Celsius could be recovered—lie as close to the surface as 3,000 to 4,000 meters in almost half the territory of the Soviet Union, and hot water at lower temperatures can be found in more than one-fifth of the country. More than 50 sites where large geothermal resources could be developed have already been identified. Nevertheless, because of high developmental costs, the Soviets currently plan to exploit geothermal resources only in especially suitable areas lacking fossil fuel resources and in some remote regions.

The main use of geothermal energy will be to provide industrial and municipal heat and hot water. Geothermal hot water is already being

Geothermal Extraction Methods

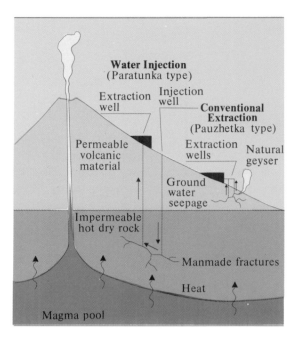

injection and extraction wells drilled to depths of 3,000 to 6,000 meters, where temperatures could reach 600 degrees Celsius.

Studies of the feasibility of using the energy of magma and hot rock to produce electricity have been done at several sites: in Kamchatka at the Avachinskaya and Mutnovskaya volcanoes, in the North Caucasus near Stavropol', and in the Carpathian Mountains near Mukachevo.

The only large-scale project now under consideration is a 200-MW installation at Mutnovskaya volcano in Kamchatka. Other ongoing geothermal projects include the development of small power plants at Kayasula (near Neftekumsk) and in Dagestan, a region where hot springs are common and where thermal waters have long been used for heating buildings. In the same region the Soviets plan to establish an Institute of Geothermal Power, which will study practical problems of building geothermal power plants.

Magnetohydrodynamic Power

The magnetohydrodynamics (MHD) process of converting thermal energy of conductor fluids directly into electricity is potentially more efficient than conventional thermal power generation in which thermal energy is converted first into mechanical energy and then into electricity. During the past 25 years, scientists in many countries have tried to design and build an economically practical MHD generator that would use the partially ionized gas produced by burning fossil fuels as the conducting fluid. This objective proved unexpectedly difficult, however, and by 1970 MHD research in France, Great Britain, West Germany, and other countries had ceased because of the projected increased costs of oil, gas, and coal. MHD research continues, nevertheless, in countries that expect to have continuing access to large supplies of coal such as Japan, Poland, the United States, and—particularly—the Soviet Union.

The USSR presently has one of the world's largest and most advanced MHD research programs. Soviet scientists are currently operating two pilot MHD power plants, the U-02 and the U-25. The former is a 75-kW generator, built in 1964 at the Academy of Sciences Institute of High Temperatures in Moscow. It is used to test materials and components later incorporated into the U-25, built in 1971 at the same institute. Both generators burned natural gas, a clean fuel that minimizes fouling. Because it is cheaper, more abundant, and produces a more conductive gas than other fossil fuels, however, coal will eventually be the primary fuel in MHD facilities, should current difficulties in converting coal to a clean gas be overcome. The U-02 has already been converted to burn coal so that the effects of slag on generator performance may be investigated. Eventually, the U-25 could also be converted to burn coal.

The United States and the Soviet Union worked closely during the 1970s on a major cooperative MHD experimental program using the Soviet facility and several US components. As part of the joint program, a second natural-gas-fired

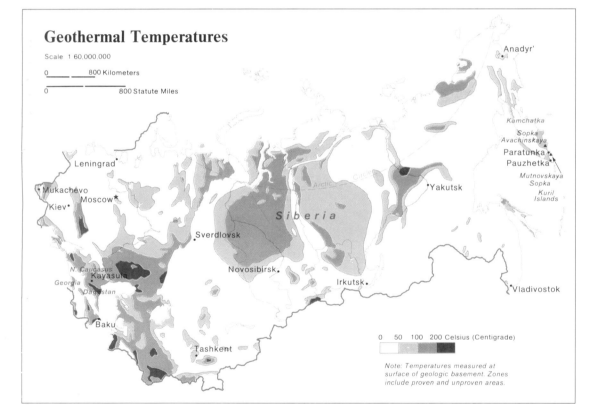

Geothermal Temperatures

Scale 1 60,000,000

0 _____ 800 Kilometers

0 _____ 800 Statute Miles

0 50 100 200 Celsius (Centigrade)

Note: Temperatures measured at surface of geologic basement. Zones include proven and unproven areas.

used to heat homes, greenhouses, and industrial buildings and to process raw wool; it is being exploited in spas and sanatoriums; and it is being injected into oil reservoirs to enhance oil recovery. Such applications have been developed in Kamchatka, the Kuril Islands, Georgia, and the North Caucasus. In Siberia, water at 70 to 100 degrees Celsius will be used to prevent freezing in placer mining operations, opening the way for year-round mining.

The only currently functioning geothermal electric power plant using steam in the Soviet Union is at Pauzhetka on the Kamchatka Peninsula. This industrial pilot plant, which exploits a deposit of saturated steam, has a rated output of 5 MW but because of its poor condition had been operating intermittently at 3.5 MW. In mid-1981 the Soviets announced that a new borehole drilled to tap additional steam will increase the station's rated capacity to 11 MW.

A 750-kW experimental power plant using a binary-cycle generating system was installed in 1968 near Paratunka, also in Kamchatka. The freon-driven turbine system used geothermal water at 80 degrees Celsius as its heat source. Although operations at the plant ceased in 1975, apparently because the Soviets were unable to cope with the high salt content of the geothermal water, steam wells still supply heat to an adjacent greenhouse farm called Termal'nyy.

Both of these power plants were built to exploit existing deposits of geothermal steam or hot water. The Soviets estimate that such deposits in Kamchatka could eventually produce as much as 600 MW. But, they estimate further, the development of artificial circulation systems in the hot rock deposits of Kamchatka could produce another 3,000 MW. This would involve using underground explosions or hydraulic pressure to create fracture zones between water

MHD generator called the U-25B was built at the U-25 facility. It incorporated a US-made superconducting magnet and was used to evaluate problems associated with the use of such high-field magnets. (Magnetic fields of the strength that will be required in commercial MHD power plants can only be produced by superconducting magnets.)

The results of these investigations will help guide the design of the U-500, a large, natural-gas-fired commercial-demonstration facility. The plant design combines MHD with a conventional steam power plant now being built in Ryazan' jointly by the Institute of High Temperatures and the Ministry of Power and Electrification. Like all future MHD power plants, it will be a hybrid facility in which a conventional power generator exploits the substantial thermal energy remaining in the conducting fluid after it has passed through an MHD generating system. Scheduled for completion in 1985, the U-500 is to combine a 250-MW MHD generating system with a 250-MW combination gas-turbine/steam-turbine generating system to achieve a total output capacity of 500 MW. If successful, plans are to construct several larger (1,000 MW) natural-gas-fired plants in other cities.

After the current studies on coal-fired MHD technology have been completed, a 500- to 1,000-MW, coal-fired demonstration plant is to be built. If successful, the plant could serve as the prototype for large numbers of such plants to be built throughout the country. In mid-1983 the Soviets announced that a 25-MW MHD generator was under construction at Estonia's Kohtla-Järve thermal power station. Reportedly, the purpose is to test the best method to adapt MHD technology to burning oil shale at high temperatures.

According to Soviet scientists, MHD topping systems could result in energy conversion efficiencies approaching 60 percent in power plants producing only electricity and 90 percent in cogeneration plants (TETs), compared with the approximately 40 percent achievable now in steam-turbine systems. Their preliminary calculations suggest that incorporating an MHD topping cycle would add only 10 or 15 percent to the cost of building a conventional thermal power plant. Some observers, however, feel that the Soviets have underestimated the difficulty and costs of overcoming the many remaining technical obstacles as well as the likely efficiency of MHD power generation.

MHD generator at the USSR Academy of Sciences Institute of High Temperatures, Moscow.

US-made MHD superconducting magnet at the Soviet Academy of Sciences Institute of High Temperatures.

Thermonuclear Fusion

The sun is so hot and dense that the matter inside it exists as a plasma of extremely rapidly moving atomic nuclei and electrons. When collisions among these nuclei are violent enough to overcome their mutual electrical repulsion, they fuse and give off highly energetic nuclear particles. Such "thermonuclear" reactions are the source of the huge energies emitted by the sun.

The awesome amounts of energy released by thermonuclear devices have attracted the interest of scientists seeking new sources of energy to generate electricity. If thermonuclear reactions could be harnessed to produce heat energy at a steady and appreciable rate in a controlled manner, fusion power plants could provide electricity virtually forever, because a prospective fuel—deuterium, an isotope of hydrogen—is in nearly inexhaustible supply. Advanced fusion research programs are under way in Western Europe, Japan, China, the United States, and the Soviet Union. Enormous technological difficulties, however, stand in the way of the economic exploitation of controlled thermonuclear reactions.

Many of the early advances in fusion research were made in the USSR; lately, however, the Soviet program has lost momentum and much of its high-level support, probably owing to the high costs associated with making further advances, coupled with the realization that the payoff, if any, is not likely to occur before the next century. Today's Soviet program, managed jointly by the Academy of Sciences and the State Committee for the Utilization of Atomic Energy, is generally less vigorous than the US program.

The essential problem in developing controlled fusion is to confine a plasma at about 100 million degrees Celsius for an extended period. Two general techniques of confinement are being pursued: *magnetic* confinement, in which a plasma is concentrated and isolated by magnetic fields; and *inertial* confinement, in which a fuel pellet is violently compressed, creating a plasma that is momentarily held together by the inertia of its inward-moving particles.

The most advanced magnetic confinement system is the *Tokamak*, a toroidal (doughnut-shaped) device invented in the USSR. Numerous Tokamaks have been built throughout the world. The Soviet Tokamaks, the T-7 and T-10, are soon to be succeeded by a larger one, the T-15. An experimental Tokamak of a size suitable for use in a thermonuclear power plant, however, would have to be much larger still.

Fusion power, if developed, will probably be used in hybrid units. Fusion produces a lot of

Experimental Soviet Tokamak, T-10.

high-energy neutrons; if these were used to breed fuel for nuclear-fission power plants, part of the cost of constructing fusion power plants could be borne by the fission power industry. Some Soviet energy engineers believe that a nuclear-fuel breeding system could be incorporated into a commercial fusion power plant around the turn of the century.

Measurement Conversion Factors

To Convert From US Measure	To Soviet Measure	Multiply by:	To Convert From Soviet Measure	To US Measure	Multiply by:
Inches	Millimeters	25.4	Millimeters	Inches	0.03937
Feet	Meters	0.3048	Meters	Feet	3.28084
Miles (statute)	Kilometers	1.609344	Kilometers	Miles (statute)	0.621371
Pounds	Kilograms	0.453592	Kilograms	Pounds	2.154623
Tons (short)	Tons (metric)	0.907185	Tons (metric)	Tons (short)	1.102311
Barrels of oil	Tons of oil	0.136986	Tons of oil	Barrels of oil	7.3
Cubic feet	Cubic meters	0.028317	Cubic meters	Cubic feet	35.314667
Barrels of oil per day	Tons of oil per year	50	Tons of oil per year	Barrels of oil per day	0.02
Barrels per day oil equivalent	Tons coal equivalent (standard fuel) per year	71.5	Tons coal equivalent (standard fuel) per year	Barrels per day oil equivalent	0.014
Btu per pound	Kilocalories per kilogram	1.8	Kilocalories per kilogram	Btu per pound	0.555556

Ultimate Recoverable Oil and Gas Reserves

The classification of Soviet oil and gas fields by size is based upon official USSR sources and Western estimates of ultimate recoverable reserves. Although the terms "supergiant" and "giant" are commonly used to quantify large oil and gas fields, there are no internationally accepted definitions of field sizes.

Supergiant fields

Oil (>5 billion barrels)

Field name	Region	Date of Discovery
Arlan	Volga-Urals	1955
Fedorovo	West Siberia	1971
Katur-Tepe	Central Asia	1956
Romashkino	Volga-Urals	1948
Samotlor	West Siberia	1966

Gas (>10 trillion cubic feet)

Field name	Region	Date of Discovery
Bovanenko	West Siberia	1971
Kharasavey	West Siberia	1974
Medvezh'ye	West Siberia	1967
Shatlyk	Central Asia	1968
Sovetabad	Central Asia	1974
Urengoy	West Siberia	1966
Yamburg	West Siberia	1969
Zapolyarnoye	West Siberia	1965

Giant fields

Oil (500 million to 5 billion barrels)

Field name	Region	Date of Discovery
Agan	West Siberia	1966
Barsa-Gel'mes	Central Asia	1962
Bavly	Volga-Urals	1946
Kholmogory	West Siberia	1973
Mamontovo	West Siberia	1965
Megion	West Siberia	1961
Mukhanovo	Volga-Urals	1945
Nebit-Dag	Central Asia	1934
Neftyanyye Kamni	Transcaucasus	1949
Novoyelkhovo	Volga-Urals	1955
Ostrov Bulla	Transcaucasus	1959
Pokachi	West Siberia	1970
Pravdinsk	West Siberia	1964
Samgori	Transcaucasus	1974
Severnyy Pokur	West Siberia	1964
Severo-Var'yegan	West Siberia	1971
Shkapovo	Volga-Urals	1953
Sovetskoye	West Siberia	1962
Tuymazy	Volga-Urals	1937
Usinsk	Timan-Pechora	1963
Ust'-Balyk	West Siberia	1961
Uzen'	North Caspian	1961
Var'yegan	West Siberia	1970
Vata	West Siberia	1961
Vat"yegan	West Siberia	1971
Vozey	Timan-Pechora	1972
Yuzhno-Sukhokumskoye	North Caucasus	1963
Zhetybay	North Caspian	1960

Gas (3 to 10 trillion cubic feet)

Field name	Region	Date of Discovery
Achak	Central Asia	1966
Arkticheskiy	West Siberia	1968
Gazli	Central Asia	1956
Gubkin	West Siberia	1965
Gugurtli	Central Asia	1965
Kandym	Central Asia	1966
Kirpichli	Central Asia	1972
Komsomol	West Siberia	1966
Layavozh	Timan-Pechora	1971
Naip	Central Asia	1970
Nakhodka	West Siberia	1974
Neyto	West Siberia	1975
Novyy Port	West Siberia	1964
Nyda	West Siberia	1972
Orenburg	Volga-Urals	1966
Pelyatka	West Siberia	1969
Pestsovyy	West Siberia	1974
Russkaya	West Siberia	1968
Sakar	Central Asia	1966
Samantepe	Central Asia	1964
Semakov	West Siberia	1971
Severo-Komsomol	West Siberia	1969
Severo-Urengoy	West Siberia	1970
Solenaya	West Siberia	1969
Sredneyamal	West Siberia	1972
Urtabulak	Central Asia	1963
Vuktyl	Timan-Pechora	1964
Vyngapur	West Siberia	1968
Yamsovey	West Siberia	1970
Yetypur	West Siberia	1971
Yubileynyy	West Siberia	1969
Yuzhno-Russkaya	West Siberia	1969
Yuzhno-Tambey	West Siberia	1974
Zapadno-Tarkosale	West Siberia	1972

Petroleum Refineries, 1 January 1984

Economic Region	Refinery Name	Economic Region	Refinery Name	Economic Region	Refinery Name
Baltic	Mažeikiai	North Caucasus (continued)	Groznyy No. 2	Urals (continued)	Perm'
Northwest	Kirishi		Groznyy No. 3		Salavat
Northern	Ukhta		Krasnodar		Ufa Novo Chernikovsk
Belorussia	Mozyr'		Tuapse		Ufa Novo Ufimskiy
	Novopolotsk	Transcaucasus	Baku No. 2		Ufa Staro Ufimskiy
Central	Konstantinovskiy		Baku Waterfront Group	Kazakhstan	Chimkent (under construction)
	Moskva (Moscow) Lyubertsy		Batumi		Gur'yev
	Ryazan'	Volga	Nizhnekamsk		Pavlodar
	Yaroslavl'		Novokuybyshevsk Lend Lease 3	Central Asia	Fergana
Ukraine	Drogobych No. 1		Novokuybyshevsk No. 2		Khamza
	Drogobych No. 2		Saratov		Krasnovodsk
	Kherson		Syzran'		Neftezavodsk (under construction)
	Kremenchug		Volgograd	West Siberia	Omsk
	Lisichansk	Volga-Vyatka	Gor'kiy 26 Bakinskikh	East Siberia	Achinsk
	L'vov		Gor'kiy (Kstovo)		Angarsk
	Nadvornaya	Urals	Ishimbay	Far East	Khabarovsk
	Odessa		Orsk		Komsomol'sk
North Caucasus	Groznyy Group		Orsk 421		

Thermal Power Plants 1,000 MW or Larger, 1 January 1984

Operational

Economic Region	Plant Name	Gross Installed Capacity (MW)
Baltic	Lithuanian	1,800
	Estonia	1,610
	Baltic	1,435
Northwest	Kirishi	2,120
Belorussia	Lukoml'	2,400
Central	Kostroma	3,600
	Ryazan'	2,800
	Konakovo	2,400
	Kashira	2,000
	Cherepet'	1,500
	TETs-23 Mosenergo Heat and Power	1,400
	TETs-22 Mosenergo Heat and Power	1,250
	TETs-21 Mosenergo Heat and Power	1,180
	Shatura	1,020
Ukraine	Zaporozh'ye	3,600
	Uglegorsk	3,600
	Krivoy Rog-2	3,000
	Burshtyn	2,400
	Zmiyëv (Gotval'd)	2,400
	Pridneprovsk	2,400
	Voroshilovgrad	2,300
	Starobeshevo	2,300
	Slavyansk	2,100
	Ladyzhin	1,800
	Tripol'ye	1,800
	Kurakhovo	1,460
Moldavia	Moldavian	2,480
North Caucasus	Novocherkassk	2,400
	Stavropol'	2,100
	Nevinnomyssk	1,380
	Krasnodar Heat and Power	1,105
Transcaucasus	Tbilisi	1,280
	Razdan	1,210
	Ali-Bayramly	1,100
Volga	Zainsk	2,400
	Lower Kama-1 Heat and Power	1,100
Urals	Reftinskiy	3,800
	Troitsk	2,500
	Iriklinskiy	2,400
	Karmanovo	1,800
	Verkhniy Tagil	1,575
	Sredneural'sk	1,198
	Yuzhno-Ural'sk	1,000
Kazakhstan	Ekibastuz-1	3,500
	Yermak	2,400
	Dzhambul	1,230
Central Asia	Syrdar'ya	3,000
	Tashkent	1,950
	Mary	1,260
	Navoi	1,250
West Siberia	Surgut-1	3,345
	Tom'-Usa	1,300
	Belovo	1,200
East Siberia	Krasnoyarsk-2	1,340
	Nazarovo	1,300
	Irkutsk-10 Heat and Power	1,160
	Krasnoyarsk Heat and Power	1,115

Under Construction

Economic Region	Plant Name
Ukraine	Zuyevka [a]
Transcaucasus	Azerbaijan [a]
Urals	Perm'
Kazakhstan	Ekibastuz-2
	South Kazakhstan (Chiganak)
Central Asia	Novo-Angren [a]
	Talimardzhan
West Siberia	Surgut-2
	Urengoy
East Siberia	Berëzovskoye-1
	Gusinoozërsk [a]
	Kharanor

[a] Currently operating at a capacity under 1,000 MW.

Hydroelectric Power Stations 1,000 MW or Larger, 1 January 1984

Operational

Station Name	Installed Capacity (MW)	River	Economic Region
Krasnoyarsk	6,000	Yenisey	East Siberia
Bratsk	4,500	Angara	East Siberia
Sayan-Shushenskoye (expansion under way)	3,840	Yenisey	East Siberia
Ust'-Ilimsk	3,840	Angara	East Siberia
Nurek	2,700	Vakhsh	Central Asia
Volga at Volgograd	2,541	Volga	Volga
Volga at Tol'yatti-Zhigulëvsk	2,300	Volga	Volga
Dnepr at Zaporozh'ye	1,538	Dnepr	Ukraine
Saratov	1,360	Volga	Volga
Inguri	1,325	Inguri	Transcaucasus
Zeya	1,290	Zeya	Far East
Toktogul'	1,200	Naryn	Central Asia
Lower Kama	1,092	Kama	Volga
Chirkey	1,075	Sulak	North Caucasus
Votkinsk	1,010	Kama	Urals

Under Construction

Station Name	River	Economic Region
Boguchany	Angara	East Siberia
Bureya	Bureya	Far East
Cheboksary [a]	Volga	Volga-Vyatka
Kaišiadorys (pump storage)	Neman, Strëva	Baltic
Rogun	Vakhsh	Central Asia
Shul'ba	Irtysh	Kazakhstan
Zagorsk (pump storage)	Kun'ya	Central

[a] Currently operating at a capacity under 1,000 MW.

Nuclear Power Stations, 1 January 1984

Operational

Station Name	Gross Installed Capacity (MW)	Date of First Operation	Type	Operating Reactors	Soviet Designation
Leningrad	4,000	1973	GMPTR	4	RBMK-1000
Chernobyl'	4,000	1977	GMPTR	4	RBMK-1000
Kursk	3,000	1976	GMPTR	3	RBMK-1000
Novovoronezhskiy	2,455	1964	PWR	1	VVER-210
			PWR	1	VVER-365
			PWR	2	VVER-440
			PWR	1	VVER-1000
Ignalina	1,500 [a]	1983	GMPTR	1	RBMK-1500 [a]
Kola	1,320	1973	PWR	3	VVER-440
Smolensk	1,000	1982	GMPTR	1	RBMK-1000
South Ukraine	1,000	1983	PWR	1	VVER-1000
Rovno	880	1979	PWR	2	VVER-440
Armenian	815 [b]	1976	PWR	2	VVER-440 [b]
Beloyarskiy	900	1964	GMPTR	1	RBMK-100
			GMPTR	1	RBMK-200
			LMFBR	1	BN-600
Bilibino ATETs	48	1974	GMPTR	4	
Total	20,168 [c]				

Under Construction

Station Name
Balakovo
Bashkir
Crimean
Gor'kiy AST
Kalinin (started up in 1984)
Khmel'nitskiy
Kostroma
Minsk ATETs
Odessa ATETs
Rostov
Tatar
Voronezh AST
Zaporozhye (started up in 1984)

[a] The RBMK-1500 represents full nameplate capacity. Of this, only one 750-MW turbo-generator was operational at the beginning of 1984.
[b] The two VVER-440 reactors are operating at 405 and 410 MW.
[c] Does not include experimental development reactors, such as Obninsk and Dimitrovgrad, or the Siberian AES and the Shevchenko AES, which do not produce commercial electric power.

Gazetteer and Index

This gazetteer and index includes names in the Soviet Union and some hydrographic and physiographic features in nearby areas.

The spelling of geographic names is in accordance with decisions of the US Board on Geographic Names (BGN). Some physiographic names and textual references to administrative divisions, however, have been simplified, and abbreviations have been used for some administrative generic terms.

Names of oil and gas fields, other than major fields, and other energy-related facilities are not normally ruled on by BGN. Their spellings are based on prevailing usage in the industry and source material. Fields producing both oil and gas are classified and named according to their production of major importance.

Coordinates for regions or areal features are given near their centers or midpoints, and streams at their mouths or lower ends.

Abbreviations

AO	Avtonomnaya Oblast'
AOk	Avtonomnyy Okrug
ASSR	Avtonomnaya Sovetskaya Sotsialisticheskaya Respublika
SSR	Sovetskaya Sotsialisticheskaya Respublika

Glossary

The following terms appear as generic parts of names in this atlas. The meanings are derived from the BGN gazetteer on the Soviet Union.

gory	mountains, mountain range
guba	bay
kanal	canal, channel, distributary
khrebet	mountains, mountain range, ridge
kryazh	ridge, hill, mountains
more	sea, sound
nagor'ye	upland, plateau, mountain range
nizmennost'	plain, lowland
ostrov(a)	island(s)
ozero	lake
peski	desert, sands
plato	plateau, upland
poluostrov	peninsula, spit
proliv	strait
sopka	volcano, mountain, mound, hill
stolovaya strana	plateau
uvaly	hills
vodokhranilishche	reservoir
vozvyshennost'	hills, upland, plateau
zaliv	gulf, bay, inlet, lagoon
zemlya	land, island(s)

Feature Designations

admd	administrative division
bay	bay
can	canal
coal	coal basin/deposit
dst	desert
gasf	gasfield
gulf	gulf
hills	hills
hydp	hydroelectric power station
iron	iron ore deposit
isl(s)	island(s)
lake	lake
mts	mountains, mountain range
nucp	nuclear power station
oilf	oilfield
oils	oil shale deposit/field
pen	peninsula
petr	petroleum refinery
pipe	oil/gas pipeline
plat	plateau
pln	plain
ppl	populated place
rdge	ridge
reg	region
resv	reservoir
rr	railroad
sea	sea
stm	stream
strt	strait
tars	tar sands deposit
thep	thermal power plant
upld	upland
u/t	uranium/thorium deposit and processing center
volc	volcano

Simplified Names

Physiographic Features

Simplified	BGN
Alay Mountains	Alayskiy Khrebet
Aldan Upland	Aldanskoye Nagor'ye
Betpak-Dala Desert	Betpak-Dala
Buzachi Peninsula	Poluostrov Buzachi
Byrranga Mountains	Gory Byrranga
Caspian Lowland	Prikaspiyskaya Nizmennost'
Central Range	Sredinnyy Khrebet
Cherskiy Range	Khrebet Cherskogo
Chukotsk Upland	Chukotskoye Nagor'ye
Chukotsk Peninsula	Chukotskiy Poluostrov
Dnepr Lowland	Pridneprovskaya Nizmennost'
Dzhugdzhur Range	Khrebet Dzhugdzhur
Gydan Peninsula	Gydanskiy Poluostrov
Karakum Desert	Peski Karakumy
Kazakh Upland	Kazakhskiy Melkosopochnik
Kolyma Lowland	Kolymskaya Nizmennost'
Kolyma Mountains	Kolymskoye Nagor'ye
Koryak Mountains	Koryakskoye Nagor'ye
Kyzylkum Desert	Kyzylkum
Lake Balkhash	Ozero Balkhash
Lena Plateau	Prilenskoye Plato
Mangyshlak Peninsula	Poluostrov Mangyshlak
Muyunkum Desert	Peski Muyunkum
North Siberian Lowland	Severo-Sibirskaya Nizmennost'
Northern Hills	Severnyye Uvaly
Oka-Don Plain	Oksko-Donskaya Nizmennost'
Sikhote-Alin' Range	Sikhote-Alin'
Stanovoy Upland	Stanovoye Nagor'ye
Stanovoy Range	Stanovoy Khrebet
Taymyr Peninsula	Poluostrov Taymyr
Taz Peninsula	Tazovskiy Poluostrov
Timan Ridge	Timanskiy Kryazh
Turan Lowland	Turanskaya Nizmennost'
Turgay Plateau	Turgayskaya Stolovaya Strana
Upper Kama Upland	Verkhnekamskaya Vozvyshennost'
Ustyurt Plateau	Plato Ustyurt
Verkhoyansk Range	Verkhoyanskiy Khrebet
Volga Upland	Privolzhskaya Vozvyshennost'
Yablonovyy Range	Yablonovyy Khrebet
Yamal Peninsula	Poluostrov Yamal

Oblast-Level Administrative Divisions

Simplified	BGN
Abkhaz ASSR	Abkhazskaya Avtonomnaya Sovetskaya Sotsialisticheskaya Respublika
Adygey AO	Adygeyskaya Avtonomnaya Oblast'
Adzhar ASSR	Adzharskaya Avtonomnaya Sovetskaya Sotsialisticheskaya Respublika
Aginskiy Buryat AOk	Aginskiy Buryatskiy Avtonomnyy Okrug
Aktyubinsk Oblast	Aktyubinskaya Oblast'
Alma-Ata Oblast	Alma-Atinskaya Oblast'
Altay Kray	Altayskiy Kray
Amur Oblast	Amurskaya Oblast'
Andizhan Oblast	Andizhanskaya Oblast'
Arkhangel'sk Oblast	Arkhangel'skaya Oblast'
Ashkhabad Oblast	Ashkhabadskaya Oblast'
Astrakhan' Oblast	Astrakhanskaya Oblast'
Bashkir ASSR	Bashkirskaya Avtonomnaya Sovetskaya Sotsialisticheskaya Respublika
Belgorod Oblast	Belgorodskaya Oblast'
Brest Oblast	Brestskaya Oblast'
Bryansk Oblast	Bryanskaya Oblast'
Bukhara Oblast	Bukharskaya Oblast'
Buryat ASSR	Buryatskaya Avtonomnaya Sovetskaya Sotsialisticheskaya Respublika
Chardzhou Oblast	Chardzhouskaya Oblast'
Chechen-Ingush ASSR	Checheno-Ingushskaya Avtonomnaya Sovetskaya Sotsialisticheskaya Respublika
Chelyabinsk Oblast	Chelyabinskaya Oblast'
Cherkassy Oblast	Cherkasskaya Oblast'
Chernigov Oblast	Chernigovskaya Oblast'
Chernovtsy Oblast	Chernovitskaya Oblast'
Chimkent Oblast	Chimkentskaya Oblast'
Chita Oblast	Chitinskaya Oblast'
Chukotsk AOk	Chukotskiy Avtonomnyy Okrug
Chuvash ASSR	Chuvashskaya Avtonomnaya Sovetskaya Sotsialisticheskaya Respublika
Dagestan ASSR	Dagestanskaya Avtonomnaya Sovetskaya Sotsialisticheskaya Respublika
Dnepropetrovsk Oblast	Dnepropetrovskaya Oblast'
Donetsk Oblast	Donetskaya Oblast'
Dzhambul Oblast	Dzhambulskaya Oblast'
Dzhezkazgan Oblast	Dzhezkazganskaya Oblast'
Dzhizak Oblast	Dzhizakskaya Oblast'
Evenk AOk	Evenkiyskiy Avtonomnyy Okrug
Fergana Oblast	Ferganskaya Oblast'
Gomel' Oblast	Gomel'skaya Oblast'
Gor'kiy Oblast	Gor'kovskaya Oblast'
Gorno-Altay AO	Gorno-Altayskaya Avtonomnaya Oblast'
Gorno-Badakhshan AO	Gorno-Badakhshanskaya Avtonomnaya Oblast'
Grodno Oblast	Grodnenskaya Oblast'
Gur'yev Oblast	Gur'yevskaya Oblast'
Irkutsk Oblast	Irkutskaya Oblast'
Issyk-Kul' Oblast	Issyk-Kul'skaya Oblast'
Ivano-Frankovsk Oblast	Ivano-Frankovskaya Oblast'
Ivanovo Oblast	Ivanovskaya Oblast'
Kabardin-Balkar ASSR	Kabardino-Balkarskaya Avtonomnaya Sovetskaya Sotsialisticheskaya Respublika
Kalinin Oblast	Kalininskaya Oblast'
Kaliningrad Oblast	Kaliningradskaya Oblast'
Kalmyk ASSR	Kalmytskaya Avtonomnaya Sovetskaya Sotsialisticheskaya Respublika
Kaluga Oblast	Kaluzhskaya Oblast'
Kamchatka Oblast	Kamchatskaya Oblast'
Karachay-Cherkes AO	Karachayevo-Cherkesskaya Avtonomnaya Oblast'
Karaganda Oblast	Karagandinskaya Oblast'
Karakalpak ASSR	Karakalpakskaya Avtonomnaya Sovetskaya Sotsialisticheskaya Respublika
Karelian ASSR	Karel'skaya Avtonomnaya Sovetskaya Sotsialisticheskaya Respublika
Kashkadar'ya Oblast	Kashkadar'inskaya Oblast'
Kemerovo Oblast	Kemerovskaya Oblast'
Khabarovsk Kray	Khabarovskiy Kray
Khakas AO	Khakasskaya Avtonomnyy Oblast'

Oblast-Level Administrative Divisions (continued)

Simplified	BGN
Khanty-Mansi AOk	Khanty-Mansiyskiy Avtonomnyy Okrug
Khar'kov Oblast	Khar'kovskaya Oblast'
Kherson Oblast	Khersonskaya Oblast'
Khmel'nitskiy Oblast	Khmel'nitskaya Oblast'
Khorezm Oblast	Khorezmskaya Oblast'
Kirov Oblast	Kirovskaya Oblast'
Kirovograd Oblast	Kirovogradskaya Oblast'
Kiyev Oblast	Kiyevskaya Oblast'
Kokchetav Oblast	Kokchetavskaya Oblast'
Komi ASSR	Komi Avtonomnaya Sovetskaya Sotsialisticheskaya Respublika
Komi-Permyak AOk	Komi-Permyatskiy Avtonomnyy Okrug
Koryak AOk	Koryakskiy Avtonomnyy Okrug
Kostroma Oblast	Kostromskaya Oblast'
Krasnodar Kray	Krasnodarskiy Kray
Krasnovodsk Oblast	Krasnovodskaya Oblast'
Krasnoyarsk Kray	Krasnoyarskiy Kray
Krym (Crimean) Oblast	Krymskaya Oblast'
Kulyab Oblast	Kulyabskaya Oblast'
Kurgan Oblast	Kurganskaya Oblast'
Kurgan-Tyube Oblast	Kurgan-Tyubinskaya Oblast'
Kursk Oblast	Kurskaya Oblast'
Kustanay Oblast	Kustanayskaya Oblast'
Kuybyshev Oblast	Kuybyshevskaya Oblast'
Kzyl-Orda Oblast	Kzyl-Ordinskaya Oblast'
Leninabad Oblast	Leninabadskaya Oblast'
Leningrad Oblast	Leningradskaya Oblast'
Lipetsk Oblast	Lipetskaya Oblast'
L'vov Oblast	L'vovskaya Oblast'
Magadan Oblast	Magadanskaya Oblast'
Mangyshlak Oblast	Mangyshlakskaya Oblast'
Mari ASSR	Mariyskaya Avtonomnaya Sovetskaya Sotsialisticheskaya Respublika
Mary Oblast	Maryyskaya Oblast'
Minsk Oblast	Minskaya Oblast'
Mogilëv Oblast	Mogilëvskaya Oblast'
Mordva ASSR	Mordovskaya Avtonomnaya Sovetskaya Sotsialisticheskaya Respublika
Moscow Oblast	Moskovskaya Oblast'
Murmansk Oblast	Murmanskaya Oblast'
Nagorno-Karabakh AO	Nagorno-Karabakhskaya Avtonomnaya Oblast'
Nakhichevan' ASSR	Nakhichevanskaya Avtonomnaya Sovetskaya Sotsialisticheskaya Respublika
Namangan Oblast	Namanganskaya Oblast'
Naryn Oblast	Narynskaya Oblast'
Navoi Oblast	Navoiyskaya Oblast'
Nenets AOk	Nenetskiy Avtonomnyy Okrug
Nikolayev Oblast	Nikolayevskaya Oblast'
Novgorod Oblast	Novgorodskaya Oblast'
Novosibirsk Oblast	Novosibirskaya Oblast'
Odessa Oblast	Odesskaya Oblast'
Omsk Oblast	Omskaya Oblast'
Orel Oblast	Orlovskaya Oblast'
Orenburg Oblast	Orenburgskaya Oblast'
Osh Oblast	Oshskaya Oblast'
Pavlodar Oblast	Pavlodarskaya Oblast'
Penza Oblast	Penzenskaya Oblast'
Perm' Oblast	Permskaya Oblast'
Poltava Oblast	Poltavskaya Oblast'
Primorskiy Kray	Primorskiy Kray
Pskov Oblast	Pskovskaya Oblast'
Rostov Oblast	Rostovskaya Oblast'
Rovno Oblast	Rovenskaya Oblast'
Ryazan' Oblast	Ryazanskaya Oblast'
Sakhalin Oblast	Sakhalinskaya Oblast'
Samarkand Oblast	Samarkandskaya Oblast'
Saratov Oblast	Saratovskaya Oblast'
Semipalatinsk Oblast	Semipalatinskaya Oblast'
Severo-Kazakhstan Oblast	Severo-Kazakhstanskaya Oblast'
Severo-Ossetin ASSR	Severo-Osetinskaya Avtonomnaya Sovetskaya Sotsialisticheskaya Respublika
Smolensk Oblast	Smolenskaya Oblast'
Stavropol' Kray	Stavropol'skiy Kray
Sumy Oblast	Sumskaya Oblast'
Surkhandar'ya Oblast	Surkhandar'inskaya Oblast'
Sverdlovsk Oblast	Sverdlovskaya Oblast'
Syrdar'ya Oblast	Syrdar'inskaya Oblast'
Talas Oblast	Talasskaya Oblast'
Taldy-Kurgan Oblast	Taldy-Kurganskaya Oblast'
Tambov Oblast	Tambovskaya Oblast'
Tashauz Oblast	Tashauzskaya Oblast'
Tashkent Oblast	Tashkentskaya Oblast'
Tatar ASSR	Tatarskaya Avtonomnaya Sovetskaya Sotsialisticheskaya Respublika
Taymyr AOk	Taymyrskiy Avtonomnyy Okrug
Ternopol' Oblast	Ternopol'skaya Oblast'
Tomsk Oblast	Tomskaya Oblast'
Tselinograd Oblast	Tselinogradskaya Oblast'
Tula Oblast	Tul'skaya Oblast'
Turgay Oblast	Turgayskaya Oblast'
Tuva ASSR	Tuvinskaya Avtonomnaya Sovetskaya Sotsialisticheskaya Respublika
Tyumen' Oblast	Tyumenskaya Oblast'
Udmurt ASSR	Udmurtskaya Avtonomnaya Sovetskaya Sotsialisticheskaya Respublika
Ul'yanovsk Oblast	Ul'yanovskaya Oblast'
Ural'sk Oblast	Ural'skaya Oblast'
Ust'-Ordynskiy Buryat AOk	Ust'-Ordynskiy Buryatskiy Avtonomnyy Okrug
Vinnitsa Oblast	Vinnitskaya Oblast'
Vitebsk Oblast	Vitebskaya Oblast'
Vladimir Oblast	Vladimirskaya Oblast'
Volgograd Oblast	Volgogradskaya Oblast'
Vologda Oblast	Vologodskaya Oblast'
Volyn' Oblast	Volynskaya Oblast'
Voronezh Oblast	Voronezhskaya Oblast'
Voroshilovgrad Oblast	Voroshilovgradskaya Oblast'
Vostochno-Kazakhstan Oblast	Vostochno-Kazakhstanskaya Oblast'
Yakut ASSR	Yakutskaya Avtonomnaya Sovetskaya Sotsialisticheskaya Respublika
Yamal-Nenets AOk	Yamalo-Nenetskiy Avtonomnyy Okrug
Yaroslavl' Oblast	Yaroslavskaya Oblast'
Yevrey AO	Yevreyskaya Avtonomnaya Oblast'
Yugo-Ossetin AO	Yugo-Osetinskaya Avtonomnaya Oblast'
Zakarpatskaya Oblast	Zakarpatskaya Oblast'
Zaporozh'ye Oblast	Zaporozhskaya Oblast'
Zhitomir Oblast	Zhitomirskaya Oblast'

Name	Feature	Latitude	Longitude	Page
A				
Abakan	ppl	53 43N	091 26E	57,RM
Aban	ppl	56 41N	096 04E	60,RM
Aban coal deposit	coal	56 30N	096 00E	60
Abaza	ppl	52 39N	090 06E	56,RM
Abkhazskaya ASSR	admd	43 00N	041 30E	79
Achak	gasf	40 59N	061 02E	21,66
Achinsk	ppl	56 17N	090 30E	57,RM
Achinsk	petr	NA	NA	31,66
Achisu	oilf	42 26N	047 45E	21
Adygeyskaya AO	admd	45 00N	040 00E	79
Adzharskaya ASSR	admd	41 40N	042 00E	79
Agan	stm	61 23N	074 35E	16,19
Agan	oilf	61 28N	076 11E	16,66
Agdam	ppl	39 59N	046 57E	56,RM
Aginskiy Buryatskiy AOk	admd	51 00N	114 30E	79
Aginskoye	ppl	51 06N	114 32E	RM
Agul	stm	55 44N	095 41E	60
Ahtme	ppl	59 18N	027 28E	44,RM
Ak-Dovurak	ppl	51 11N	090 36E	56,RM
Ak-Tyuz-Bordunskiy uranium/thorium deposit	u/t	NA	NA	42,43
Akhtubinsk	ppl	48 16N	046 10E	RM
Aksënovo-Zilovskoye	ppl	53 04N	117 32E	RM
Aksu	ppl	52 30N	071 59E	56,RM
Aksuyëk	ppl	44 45N	074 21E	RM
Aksuyëk-Kiyakhty uranium deposit	u/t	NA	NA	42,43
Aktas	oilf	43 07N	051 57E	21
Aktogay	ppl	46 57N	079 40E	RM
Aktyubinsk	ppl	50 17N	057 10E	56,79,RM
Aktyubinskaya Oblast'	admd	48 00N	058 00E	79
Aktyuz	ppl	42 54N	076 07E	RM
Al'met'yevsk	ppl	54 53N	052 20E	20,RM
Alapayevsk	ppl	57 50N	061 41E	RM
Alay Mountains	mts	39 45N	072 00E	RM
Alazeya	stm	70 51N	153 34E	RM
Aldan	ppl	58 37N	125 24E	11,57,59,RM
Aldan	stm	63 28N	129 35E	11,RM
Aldan uranium/thorium deposit	u/t	NA	NA	42,43
Aldan Upland	upld	57 00N	127 00E	11,RM
Alekhin	oilf	62 26N	071 30E	16
Aleksandriya	ppl	48 40N	033 07E	RM
Aleksandriya coal deposit	coal	48 39N	033 03E	34
Aleksandrov Gay	ppl	50 09N	048 34E	32,56,RM
Aleksandrovsk coal region	coal	50 00N	142 45E	34
Aleksandrovsk-Sakhalinskiy	ppl	50 54N	142 10E	57,RM
Alekseyevka	oilf	52 34N	051 07E	20
Alenkin	oilf	60 29N	077 10E	16
Aleysk	ppl	52 28N	082 45E	RM
Ali-Bayramly	ppl	39 55N	048 56E	RM
Ali-Bayramly	thep	NA	NA	49,67
Alma-Ata	ppl	43 15N	076 57E	32,55,56,79,RM
Alma-Atinskaya Oblast'	admd	44 00N	076 00E	79
Almalyk	ppl	40 50N	069 35E	RM
Altai Mountains	mts	48 00N	090 00E	RM
Altayskiy Kray	admd	52 30N	083 00E	79
Alushta	ppl	44 40N	034 25E	62,RM
Alyab'yevo	oilf	53 15N	053 48E	20
Alytus	ppl	54 24N	024 03E	RM
Amangel'dy	ppl	50 10N	065 13E	56,RM
Amderma	ppl	69 45N	061 39E	RM
Amga	stm	62 38N	134 32E	11,RM
Amgun'	stm	52 56N	139 38E	11,RM
Amu Darya	stm	43 40N	059 01E	21,RM
Amur	stm	52 56N	141 10E	11,RM
Amursk	ppl	50 14N	136 54E	RM
Amurskaya Oblast'	admd	54 00N	128 00E	79
Anabar	stm	73 08N	113 36E	RM
Anadyr'	ppl	64 45N	177 29E	57,59,RM
Anadyr'	stm	64 54N	176 13E	RM
Anadyr' coal basin	coal	65 00N	174 00E	34,40
Anadyr' coal deposit	coal	65 00N	177 30E	34
Anadyrskiy Zaliv	gulf	64 00N	178 00W	RM
Andizhan	ppl	40 45N	072 22E	56,79,RM
Andizhanskaya Oblast'	admd	40 45N	072 00E	79
Andropov	ppl	58 03N	038 50E	32,RM
Angara	stm	58 06N	093 00E	50,51,60,67,RM
Angarsk	ppl	52 34N	103 54E	RM
Angarsk	petr	NA	NA	31,66
Angren	ppl	41 01N	070 12E	60,RM
Angren coal deposit	coal	41 09N	070 00E	34
Anzhero-Sudzhensk	ppl	56 07N	086 01E	60,RM
Anzhero-Sudzhensk coal deposit	coal	56 10N	086 00E	34
Apatity	ppl	67 34N	033 22E	RM
April 28	oilf	39 52N	050 50E	21
Aral Sea	sea	45 00N	060 00E	RM
Aral'sk	ppl	46 48N	061 40E	56,59,RM
Aras	stm	39 59N	048 20E	21
Arenets	gasf	64 51N	057 43E	20
Argun	stm	53 20N	121 28E	RM
Ariadnoye	ppl	45 09N	134 21E	RM
Arkagala	ppl	63 09N	146 47E	57,59,RM
Arkagala coal deposit	coal	63 25N	147 00E	34
Arkalyk	ppl	50 13N	066 50E	79,RM
Arkhangel'sk	ppl	64 34N	040 32E	56,59,79,RM
Arkhangel'skaya Oblast'	admd	64 00N	044 00E	79
Arkticheskiy	gasf	69 46N	070 49E	16,66
Arlan	oilf	55 59N	054 13E	20,22,66
Armavir	ppl	45 00N	041 08E	RM
Armenian	nucp	NA	NA	52,67
Armenian SSR	admd	40 00N	045 00E	21,79
Arsen'yev	ppl	44 10N	133 15E	RM
Artëm	ppl	43 22N	132 13E	RM
Artëm	oilf	40 28N	050 22E	21
Artëm coal deposit	coal	43 30N	132 19E	34
Artëmovsk	ppl	54 21N	093 26E	57,RM
Artëmovskiy coal deposit	coal	57 30N	061 30E	34
Arys'	ppl	42 26N	068 48E	56,RM
Arzamas	ppl	55 23N	043 50E	56,RM
Asar	gasf	43 30N	052 33E	21
Ashkhabad	ppl	37 57N	058 23E	21,56,61,79,RM
Ashkhabadskaya Oblast'	admd	39 00N	059 00E	79
Asino	ppl	57 00N	086 09E	RM
Askiz	ppl	53 08N	090 32E	56,RM
Astara	ppl	38 26N	048 53E	21,56,RM
Astrakhan'	ppl	46 21N	048 03E	21,25,55,56,79,RM
Astrakhan'	gasf	46 58N	048 16E	21,23
Astrakhanskaya Oblast'	admd	47 00N	048 00E	79
Atabay	gasf	39 54N	058 33E	21
Atbasar	ppl	51 48N	068 20E	RM
Atlasovo	ppl	46 01N	142 09E	RM
Avachinskaya, Sopka	volc	53 15N	158 49E	64,RM
Ay-Pim	oilf	62 17N	071 06E	16
Ay-Yuan	oilf	59 27N	072 45E	16
Ayaguz	ppl	47 56N	080 23E	56,RM

Name	Feature	Latitude	Longitude	Page
A (continued)				
Aykhal	ppl	66 00N	111 30E	57,59,RM
Ayon, Ostrov	isl	66 50N	168 40E	RM
Aysarinskoye	ppl	53 16N	071 46E	56,RM
Azerbaijan	thep	NA	NA	49,67
Azerbaijan SSR	admd	40 30N	047 30E	21,22,79
Azov, Sea of	sea	46 00N	036 00E	RM
B				
Bagadzha	gasf	39 00N	062 40E	21
Bagdarin	ppl	54 26N	113 36E	RM
Baikal-Amur Mainline (BAM)	rr	56 30N	118 00E	11,RM
Baikal, Lake	lake	54 00N	109 00E	RM
Bakanas	ppl	44 50N	076 15E	56,RM
Bakhar	oilf	40 00N	050 00E	21
Baku	ppl	40 23N	049 51E	21,32,55,56,79, RM
Baku No. 2	petr	NA	NA	30,31,66
Baku Waterfront Group	petr	NA	NA	31,66
Balagannakh	ppl	64 30N	143 50E	57,RM
Balakovo	ppl	52 02N	047 47E	RM
Balakovo	nucp	NA	NA	52,67
Balashov	ppl	51 32N	043 08E	RM
Balkhash	ppl	46 50N	074 58E	56,RM
Balkhash, Lake	lake	46 00N	074 00E	RM
Baltic	thep	NA	NA	49,67
Baltic oil and gas region	reg	55 00N	022 00E	14,25,32
Baltic oil shale deposit	oils	59 04N	028 17E	44
Baltic Economic Region	reg	56 00N	025 00E	79
Baltic Sea	sea	56 00N	018 00E	RM
Baltiysk	ppl	54 39N	019 55E	RM
Bambuyka	ppl	55 48N	115 47E	59,RM
Bamovskaya	ppl	54 08N	123 42E	11,RM
Barabinsk	ppl	55 21N	078 21E	RM
Baranovichi	ppl	53 08N	026 02E	RM
Barents Sea	sea	74 00N	036 00E	RM
Barguzin	stm	53 37N	109 37E	57,RM
Barinovka	oilf	52 58N	050 43E	20
Barnaul	ppl	53 22N	083 45E	55,56,79,RM
Barsa-Gel'mes	oilf	39 04N	054 00E	21,66
Bashkir	nucp	NA	NA	52,67
Bashkirskaya ASSR	admd	54 00N	056 00E	20,79
Bastryk	oilf	55 23N	052 21E	20
Batagay	ppl	67 38N	134 38E	RM
Batumi	ppl	41 38N	041 38E	21,32,55,56,79,RM
Batumi	petr	NA	NA	31,66
Batyrbay	oilf	56 49N	055 55E	20
Bavly	oilf	54 30N	053 11E	20,66
Baydaratskaya Guba	bay	69 00N	067 30E	16
Baykal	ppl	51 53N	104 47E	RM
Baykonur	ppl	47 50N	066 03E	56,RM
Bayram-Ali	ppl	37 50N	062 06E	RM
Bayram-Ali	gasf	37 50N	062 06E	21
Bekabad	ppl	40 13N	069 14E	RM
Bekdash	ppl	41 34N	052 32E	56,RM
Bel'kovskiy, Ostrov	isl	75 32N	135 44E	RM
Bel'tsy	ppl	47 46N	027 56E	56,RM
Belaya	stm	55 54N	053 33E	20,RM
Belaya Tserkov'	ppl	49 47N	030 07E	RM
Belebey	oilf	54 10N	053 55E	20
Belgorod	ppl	50 36N	036 34E	79,RM
Belgorod-Dnestrovskiy	ppl	46 12N	030 21E	RM
Belgorodskaya Oblast'	admd	50 45N	037 30E	79
Belogorsk	ppl	50 55N	128 28E	RM
Belogorsk	ppl	55 02N	088 28E	60,RM
Belokurikha	ppl	51 59N	084 59E	RM
Belomorsk	ppl	64 32N	034 48E	RM
Beloretsk	ppl	53 58N	058 24E	RM
Belorussia Economic Region	reg	53 00N	028 00E	79
Belorussian oil shale deposit	oils	53 46N	029 14E	44
Belorussian SSR	admd	53 00N	028 00E	79
Belovo	ppl	54 25N	086 18E	38,RM
Belovo	thep	NA	NA	49,67
Beloyarskiy	ppl	56 45N	061 24E	RM
Beloyarskiy	ppl	63 43N	066 40E	16,RM
Beloyarskiy	nucp	NA	NA	52,67
Belyy Yar	ppl	58 26N	085 01E	60,RM
Belyy, Ostrov	isl	73 10N	070 45E	RM
Bendery	ppl	46 49N	029 29E	RM
Bennetta, Ostrov	isl	76 21N	148 56E	RM
Benoy	oilf	42 42N	046 29E	21
Berdsk	ppl	54 47N	083 02E	RM
Berdyansk	ppl	46 45N	036 47E	RM
Berdyanskoye	gasf	51 14N	055 05E	20
Berezniki	ppl	59 24N	056 46E	RM
Berëzovo	ppl	63 56N	065 02E	16,23,RM
Berëzovo	gasf	63 36N	064 24E	16
Berëzovo oil shale deposit	oils	65 32N	062 48E	44
Berëzovskoye	ppl	55 50N	089 36E	60,RM
Berëzovskoye coal deposit	coal	55 45N	089 15E	34,60
Berëzovskoye-1	thep	NA	NA	49,60,67
Berëzovyy	ppl	51 40N	135 42E	RM
Bering Sea	sea	60 00N	175 00W	RM
Bering Strait	strt	66 00N	169 00W	RM
Beringovskiy	ppl	63 03N	179 19E	RM
Beringovskiy coal deposit	coal	63 00N	178 40E	34
Berkakit	ppl	56 34N	124 48E	11,RM
Beshkul'	oilf	46 13N	046 34E	21
Bestyakh	ppl	61 24N	128 50E	32,RM
Betpak-Dala Desert	dst	46 00N	070 00E	RM
Beurdeshik	gasf	39 17N	060 36E	21
Beyneu	ppl	45 11N	055 06E	21,32,56,59,RM
Bezmein	ppl	38 05N	058 12E	21,RM
Bidzhan	ppl	47 58N	131 56E	57,RM
Bikin	ppl	46 48N	134 16E	57,RM
Bikin coal deposit	coal	46 53N	134 14E	34
Bilibino	ppl	68 03N	166 20E	57,59,RM
Bilibino ATETs	nucp	NA	NA	52,67
Binagadi tar sands deposit	tars	40 05N	048 57E	45
Birobidzhar	ppl	48 48N	137 57E	57,RM
Biryusa	stm	57 43N	095 24E	60
Biya	stm	52 25N	085 00E	RM
Biysk	ppl	52 34N	085 15E	56,RM
Black Sea	sea	43 00N	035 00E	RM
Blagoveshchensk	ppl	50 16N	127 32E	79,RM
Blagoyevo	ppl	63 25N	074 56E	RM
Bobrovka	oilf	52 32N	051 36E	20
Bobruysk	ppl	53 09N	029 14E	RM
Bodaybo	ppl	57 51N	114 10E	RM
Boguchany	ppl	58 23N	097 29E	RM
Boguchany	hydp	NA	NA	50,67
Bol'shaya Kuonamka	stm	70 45N	113 24E	RM
Bol'shevik, Ostrov	isl	78 40N	102 30E	RM
Bol'shoy Anyuy	stm	68 30N	160 49E	RM
Bol'shoy Begichëv, Ostrov	isl	74 20N	112 30E	RM

Name	Feature	Latitude	Longitude	Page
B (continued)				
Bol'shoy Lyakhovskiy, Ostrov	isl	73 35N	142 00E	RM
Bol'shoy Pit	stm	59 01N	091 44E	60
Bol'shoy Yugan	stm	61 01N	073 24E	16,RM
Bolbgoye	ppl	57 24N	034 02E	56,RM
Bordyuzhskiy	oilf	55 58N	052 25E	20
Bor	ppl	56 22N	044 03E	RM
Borisoglebsk	ppl	51 23N	042 06E	RM
Borisov	ppl	54 15N	028 30E	RM
Borodino	ppl	55 55N	094 55E	60,RM
Borovichi	ppl	58 24N	033 55E	RM
Borovka	oilf	54 07N	051 19E	20
Borzya	ppl	50 24N	116 31E	57,RM
Bovanenko	gasf	70 25N	068 19E	15,16,17,23,66
Bortyshka (Boltyshka) oil shale deposit	oils	48 37N	033 29E	44
Bratsk	ppl	56 21N	101 55E	55,57,59,60,RM
Bratsk	hydp	NA	NA	50,51,58,67
Bratskoye Vodokhranilishche	resv	56 05N	101 50E	60,RM
Brest	ppl	52 06N	023 42E	32,56,79,RM
Brestskaya Oblast'	admd	52 30N	025 30E	79
Brezhnev	ppl	55 42N	052 19E	RM
Bryansk	ppl	55 15N	034 22E	56,79,RM
Bryanskaya Oblast'	admd	53 00N	033 30E	79
Budennovsk	ppl	44 46N	044 12E	56,RM
Bugul'ma	ppl	54 33N	052 48E	56,RM
Buguruslan	ppl	53 39N	052 26E	RM
Buguruslan	oilf	53 39N	052 32E	20
Bukachacha	ppl	52 59N	116 55E	RM
Bukachacha coal deposit	coal	53 00N	117 00E	34
Bukhara	ppl	39 48N	064 25E	21,56,61,62,79
Bukharskaya Oblast'	admd	41 00N	064 00E	79
Buila-More	gasf	39 45N	049 49E	21
Buor-Khaya, Guba	bay	71 30N	131 00E	RM
Bureya	stm	49 27N	129 30E	50,51,67
Bureya	hydp	NA	NA	50,67
Bureya coal basin	coal	51 00N	132 30E	34,40
Burkand'ya	ppl	63 19N	147 30E	RM
Burshtyn	ppl	49 16N	024 38E	RM
Burshtyn	thep	NA	NA	49,67
Buryatskaya ASSR	admd	53 00N	109 00E	79
Buy	ppl	58 29N	041 30E	RM
Buzachi Peninsula	pen	45 00N	052 00E	21,RM
Buzuluk	ppl	52 47N	052 15E	RM
Byrranga Mountains	mts	75 00N	104 00E	RM
Bystrin	oilf	61 37N	072 53E	16
Byrantay	stm	68 46N	134 20E	RM
C				
Carpathian Mountains	mts	47 00N	025 30E	RM
Caspian Lowland	pln	48 00N	052 00E	RM
Caspian Sea	sea	42 00N	050 00E	21,RM
Caucasus Mountains	mts	42 00N	045 00E	21,RM
Center power system	reg	54 00N	038 00E	46,55
Central coal region	coal	48 00N	142 15E	34
Central Asia oil and gas region	reg	40 00N	060 00E	14,15,21,22,23, 25,32
Central Asia power system	reg	40 00N	068 00E	46,55
Central Asia Economic Region	reg	39 00N	066 00E	79
Central Chernozem Economic Region	reg	51 00N	040 00E	79
Central Economic Region	reg	56 00N	038 00E	79
Central Range	mts	56 00N	158 00E	RM
Central Russian Upland	upld	52 00N	038 00E	RM
Central Siberian Plateau	plat	66 00N	106 00E	RM
Chadan	ppl	51 17N	091 35E	RM
Chaladidi	oilf	42 06N	041 49E	21
Chany, Ozero	lake	54 50N	077 30E	RM
Chara	stm	60 22N	120 50E	RM
Chardzhou	ppl	39 06N	063 34E	21,56,79,RM
Chardzhouskaya Oblast'	admd	39 00N	063 00E	79
Charkesar uranium deposit	u/t	NA	NA	42,43
Charsk	ppl	49 34N	081 05E	56,RM
Chaun-Chukotka coal area	coal	66 30N	178 00E	34
Chavlisay-Krasnogorskiy-Yangiabad uranium deposit	u/t	NA	NA	42,43
Chayek	ppl	41 55N	074 30E	56,RM
Chaykovskiy	ppl	56 47N	054 09E	RM
Chayvo	oilf	52 31N	143 46E	11
Chebach'ye	oilf	60 27N	078 47E	16
Cheboksary	ppl	56 09N	047 15E	56,79,RM
Cheboksary	hydp	NA	NA	50,51,67
Checheno-Ingushskaya ASSR	admd	43 15N	045 30E	21,79
Chegdomyn	ppl	51 10N	133 05E	57,RM
Chekmagush	oilf	55 12N	054 44E	20
Cheleken	ppl	39 26N	053 07E	56,RM
Cheleken	oilf	39 14N	053 27E	21
Chelkar	ppl	47 50N	059 36E	56,59,RM
Chelny	ppl	48 53N	136 02E	RM
Chelyabinsk	ppl	55 10N	061 24E	32,55,56,79,RM
Chelyabinsk coal basin	coal	52 00N	062 15E	34
Chelyabinskaya Oblast'	admd	54 00N	060 30E	79
Cheremkhovo	ppl	53 09N	103 05E	57,RM
Cheremkhovo coal deposit	coal	53 00N	102 30E	34
Cheremkhovo oil shale deposit	oils	53 59N	101 41E	44
Cheremshan	oilf	54 44N	051 28E	20
Cherëmushki	ppl	52 52N	091 24E	RM
Cherepet'	ppl	54 07N	036 23E	RM
Cherepet'	thep	NA	NA	49,67
Cherepovets	ppl	59 08N	037 54E	56,RM
Cherkasskaya Oblast'	admd	49 00N	032 00E	79
Cherkassy	ppl	49 26N	032 04E	79,RM
Cherkessk	ppl	44 14N	042 03E	RM
Chermoz	oilf	58 49N	056 00E	20
Chernigov	ppl	51 30N	031 18E	79,RM
Chernigovskaya Oblast'	admd	51 00N	032 00E	79
Chernobyl'	ppl	51 16N	030 14E	RM
Chernobyl'	nucp	NA	NA	52,67
Chernogorsk	ppl	53 49N	091 18E	RM
Chernogorsk coal deposit	coal	53 45N	091 00E	34
Chernovitskaya Oblast'	admd	48 15N	026 00E	79
Chernovskiye Kopi coal deposit	coal	52 05N	112 45E	34
Chernovtsy	ppl	48 18N	025 56E	56,79,RM
Chernyakhovsk	ppl	54 38N	021 49E	RM
Chernyayevo	ppl	52 46N	125 59E	RM
Chernyshevsk	ppl	52 32N	117 00E	57,RM
Chernyshevskiy	ppl	62 59N	112 35E	57,58,59,RM
Cherskiy	ppl	68 45N	161 18E	57,RM
Cherskiy Range	mts	65 00N	144 00E	RM
Chervonograd	ppl	50 23N	024 14E	RM
Cheshakaya Guba	bay	67 30N	046 30E	20,RM
Chib'yu	oilf	63 56N	053 44E	20
Chiganak	ppl	45 06N	073 58E	48,RM
Chigirik uranium processing center	u/t	NA	NA	42,43
Chiili	ppl	44 10N	066 45E	56,RM
Chimkent	ppl	42 18N	069 36E	32,56,79,RM

Name	Feature	Latitude	Longitude	Page
C (continued)				
Chimkent	petr	NA	NA	31,66
Chimkentskaya Oblast'	admd	43 00N	068 00E	79
Chirchik	ppl	41 29N	069 35E	61,62,RM
Chirkey	hydp	NA	NA	50,67
Chistopol'	ppl	55 21N	050 37E	RM
Chita	ppl	52 03N	113 30E	57,79,RM
Chitinskaya Oblast'	admd	52 00N	117 00E	79
Chkalovsk uranium deposit/processing center	u/t	NA	NA	42,43
Chokurdakh	ppl	70 38N	147 55E	RM
Chu	ppl	43 36N	073 42E	56,RM
Chuguyevka	ppl	44 10N	133 52E	57,RM
Chukchi Sea	sea	69 00N	174 00W	RM
Chukotsk Peninsula	pen	66 00N	174 00W	RM
Chukotsk Upland	mts	67 00N	176 00E	RM
Chukotskiy AOk	admd	67 30N	170 00E	79
Chul'man	ppl	56 52N	124 52E	11,57,RM
Chul'man coal deposit	coal	56 45N	125 00E	11,34
Chulym	ppl	55 06N	080 58E	56,RM
Chulym	stm	57 43N	083 51E	60,RM
Chuna	stm	57 47N	094 37E	60,RM
Chuna tar sands deposit	tars	57 35N	097 12E	45
Chunya	stm	61 36N	096 30E	RM
Chupa	ppl	66 16N	033 04E	RM
Chupa District uranium deposit	u/t	NA	NA	42,43
Chupal'skoye	oilf	60 04N	072 38E	16
Chusovaya	stm	58 13N	056 22E	20
Chusovoy	ppl	58 17N	057 49E	56,RM
Chutyr'	oilf	57 26N	053 12E	20
Chuvashskaya ASSR	admd	55 30N	047 00E	79
Chuya	stm	50 24N	086 39E	RM
Crimea	nucp	NA	NA	52,67
Crimean Peninsula	pen	45 00N	034 00E	RM
D				
Dagestanskaya ASSR	admd	43 00N	047 00E	21,64,79
Dal'mamedly	oilf	40 40N	045 59E	21
Dal'negorsk	ppl	44 35N	135 35E	57,RM
Dal'nerechensk	ppl	45 55N	133 40E	RM
Dalakhay	ppl	50 50N	102 48E	RM
Danilov	ppl	58 12N	040 10E	RM
Danilov	oilf	60 56N	064 05E	16
Daugava	stm	57 00N	024 00E	RM
Daugavpils	ppl	55 53N	026 32E	RM
De-Kastri	ppl	51 28N	140 47E	RM
Debin	ppl	62 22N	150 12E	57,RM
Dekabr'skoye	oilf	62 08N	070 06E	16
Dëma	stm	54 42N	056 00E	20
Demskoye	oilf	53 40N	054 11E	20
Denau	ppl	38 16N	067 54E	56,RM
Dengizkul'	gasf	39 28N	064 40E	21
Deputatskiy	ppl	69 18N	138 54E	RM
Derbent	ppl	42 03N	048 18E	RM
Desna	stm	50 33N	030 32E	RM
Desovskoye iron ore deposit	iron	57 30N	124 15E	11
Dikson	ppl	73 30N	080 35E	59,RM
Dimitrovgrad	ppl	54 14N	049 33E	RM
Dimitrovgrad	nucp	NA	NA	67
Dmitriya Lapteva, Proliv	strt	73 00N	142 00E	RM
Dnepr	stm	43 30N	032 18E	50,51,67,RM
Dnepr at Zaporozh'ye	hydp	NA	NA	50,67
Dnepr coal basin	coal	48 00N	032 00E	34,40
Dnepr Lowland	pln	50 00N	032 00E	RM
Dnepr Upland	upld	49 00N	028 00E	RM
Dnepropetrovsk	ppl	48 27N	034 59E	56,79,RM
Dnepropetrovskaya Oblast'	admd	48 30N	035 00E	79
Dnestr	stm	46 18N	030 17E	RM
Dno	ppl	57 50N	029 59E	RM
Dolgozhdannoye coal deposit	coal	68 00N	172 30E	34
Dolina	ppl	48 58N	024 01E	RM
Dolinsk	ppl	47 21N	142 48E	57,RM
Don	stm	47 04N	039 18E	53,RM
Donets coal basin	coal	48 00N	039 00E	34,35,36,37,38 40,41
Donetsk	ppl	48 00N	037 48E	55,56,79,RM
Donetsk coal deposit	coal	47 50N	037 50E	34
Donetskaya Oblast'	admd	48 00N	037 30E	79
Dorokhovka	oilf	56 38N	056 57E	20
Dossor	ppl	47 32N	053 00E	56,RM
Dossor	oilf	47 34N	052 56E	21
Drogobych No. 1	petr	NA	NA	31,66
Drogobych No. 2	petr	NA	NA	31,66
Drovyanaya	ppl	51 53N	113 02E	RM
Druzhba	ppl	45 17N	082 30E	RM
Dubinino	ppl	55 40N	089 06E	60,RM
Dudinka	ppl	69 25N	086 15E	16,57,RM
Dukat	ppl	62 45N	155 15E	RM
Dulgalakh	stm	67 44N	133 12E	RM
Dunay	ppl	42 52N	132 22E	RM
Dushanbe	ppl	38 33N	068 48E	55,56,79,RM
Dzerzhinsk	ppl	56 15N	043 24E	RM
Dzh'yer	oilf	63 17N	054 58E	20
Dzhalal-Abad	ppl	40 56N	073 00E	RM
Dzhalinda	ppl	53 29N	123 54E	11,RM
Dzhambul	ppl	42 54N	071 22E	56,79,RM
Dzhambul	thep	NA	NA	49,67
Dzhambulskaya Oblast'	admd	44 00N	072 00E	79
Dzhansugurov	ppl	45 24N	079 29E	56,RM
Dzhebariki-Khaya coal deposit	coal	62 25N	136 30E	34
Dzhebol'	gasf	62 26N	056 30E	20
Dzhergalan coal deposit	coal	42 33N	079 03E	34
Dzhetygara	ppl	52 11N	061 12E	56,RM
Dzhezkazgan	ppl	47 47N	067 46E	56,59,RM
Dzhezkazganskaya Oblast'	admd	47 30N	071 00E	79
Dzhizak	ppl	40 06N	067 50E	79,RM
Dzhizakskaya Oblast'	admd	40 30N	067 40E	79
Dzhugdzhur Range	mts	58 00N	136 00E	RM
Dzhul'fa	ppl	38 57N	045 38E	RM
E				
East Kamchatka coal area	coal	56 00N	162 00E	34
East Siberia Economic Region	reg	61 00N	099 00E	79
East Siberian oil and gas region	reg	64 00N	126 00E	14,15,25,32
East Siberian Sea	sea	74 00N	166 00E	RM
Egvekinot	ppl	66 19N	179 10W	57,59,RM
Ekibastuz	ppl	51 40N	075 22E	55,56,RM
Ekibastuz coal basin	coal	51 30N	075 30E	34,35,36,37,38 39,40
Ekibastuz-1	thep	NA	NA	47,48,49,55,67
Ekibastuz-2	thep	NA	NA	49,67
El'dikan	ppl	60 48N	135 11E	59,RM
El'ginskiy	ppl	64 35N	141 47E	RM

Name	Feature	Latitude	Longitude	Page
E (continued)				
Elitsa	ppl	46 16N	044 14E	21,56,79,RM
Emba	ppl	48 50N	058 08E	56,RM
Emba	stm	46 38N	053 14E	21
Emba/Caspian tar sands deposit	tars	47 47N	050 10E	45
Engel's	ppl	51 30N	046 07E	RM
Erozionnyy	ppl	65 46N	149 44E	RM
Erzin	ppl	50 15N	095 10E	57,RM
Estonia	thep	NA	NA	44,49,67
Estonian oil shale field	oils	59 07N	027 23E	44
Estonian SSR	admd	59 00N	026 00E	79
Evenkiyskiy AOk	admd	65 00N	095 00E	79
Export pipeline	pipe	55 45N	049 00E	10,11,20,32,33
F				
Far East power system	reg	51 00N	134 00E	46,55
Far East Economic Region	reg	63 00N	143 00E	79
Farab	gasf	39 16N	063 27E	21
Fedorovo	oilf	61 40N	073 32E	16,17,22,29,66
Fergana	ppl	40 23N	071 46E	79,RM
Fergana	petr	NA	NA	31,66
Fergana Valley tar sands deposit	tars	42 41N	073 21E	45
Ferganskaya Oblast'	admd	40 30N	071 30E	79
Fevral'sk	ppl	52 28N	130 43E	RM
Finland, Gulf of	gulf	60 00N	027 00E	RM
Fominovka	oilf	54 13N	053 09E	20
Fort-Shevchenko	ppl	44 31N	050 16E	RM
Franz Josef Land	isls	81 00N	055 00E	RM
Franz Josef Land tar sands deposit	tars	80 30N	049 00E	45
Frolovo	ppl	49 46N	043 40E	RM
Frunze	ppl	42 54N	074 36E	55,56,79,RM
G				
Gayny	ppl	60 18N	054 19E	56,RM
Gayvoron	ppl	48 21N	029 51E	56,RM
Gazli	ppl	40 14N	063 24E	56,RM
Gazli	gasf	40 04N	063 21E	21,66
Genriyetty, Ostrov	isl	77 06N	156 30E	RM
Georga, Zemlya	isl	80 30N	049 00E	RM
Georgian SSR	admd	42 00N	043 30E	21,79
Georgiu-Dezh	ppl	50 59N	039 30E	56,RM
Georgiyevsk	ppl	44 09N	042 28E	RM
Geral'd, Ostrov	isl	71 23N	175 40W	RM
Gilyuy	stm	53 58N	127 28E	11,RM
Glazov	ppl	58 09N	052 40E	RM
Gogran'dag	gasf	38 44N	054 27E	21
Gomel'	ppl	52 25N	031 00E	56,79,RM
Gomel'skaya Oblast'	admd	52 00N	030 00E	79
Gonam	stm	57 21N	131 14E	11
Gor'kiy	ppl	56 20N	044 00E	32,56,79,RM
Gor'kiy (Kstovo)	petr	NA	NA	31,66
Gor'kiy AST	nucp	NA	NA	52,53,67
Gor'kiy 26 Bakinskiy	petr	NA	NA	31,66
Gor'kovskaya Oblast'	admd	56 00N	045 00E	79
Gori	ppl	41 48N	044 07E	RM
Gorlovka	ppl	48 18N	038 03E	RM
Gorno-Altaysk	ppl	51 58N	085 58E	56,RM
Gorno-Altayskaya AO	admd	51 00N	086 00E	79
Gorno-Badakhshanskaya AO	admd	38 00N	073 00E	79
Gornozavodsk	ppl	46 34N	141 49E	57,RM
Gornyak	ppl	51 00N	081 29E	RM
Goryachegorsk	ppl	55 24N	088 55E	60,RM
Gotval'd	ppl	49 41N	036 21E	RM
Gozhan	oilf	56 31N	055 08E	20
Grakhovo	oilf	56 04N	051 55E	20
Granitogorsk	ppl	42 44N	073 27E	RM
Granitogorsk uranium deposit/processing center	u/t	NA	NA	42,43
Greem-Bell, Ostrov	isl	81 10N	064 00E	RM
Gremikha	oilf	56 52N	053 48E	20
Grodnenskaya Oblast'	admd	53 30N	024 30E	79
Grodno	ppl	53 41N	023 50E	79,RM
Groznyy	ppl	43 20N	045 42E	21,56,79,RM
Groznyy tar sands deposit	tars	44 23N	044 44E	45
Groznyy Group	petr	NA	NA	31,66
Groznyy No. 2	petr	NA	NA	31,66
Groznyy No. 3	petr	NA	NA	31,66
Gryazi	ppl	52 30N	040 00E	RM
Gubino	oilf	53 18N	048 41E	20
Gubkin	ppl	51 17N	037 32E	56,RM
Gubkin	gasf	64 45N	077 14E	16,66
Gubkin	gasf	39 33N	052 22E	21
Gudermes	oilf	43 05N	046 20E	21
Gugurtli	gasf	40 04N	062 16E	21,66
Gulistan	ppl	40 29N	068 46E	79,RM
Gun"yegan	oilf	61 41N	077 46E	16
Gur'yev	ppl	47 07N	051 53E	21,32,56,59,79, RM
Gur'yev	petr	NA	NA	31,66
Gur'yevskaya Oblast'	admd	45 00N	053 00E	79
Gus'-Khrustal'nyy	ppl	55 37N	040 40E	RM
Gusinoozërsk	ppl	51 17N	106 30E	57,RM
Gusinoozërsk	thep	NA	NA	49,67
Gusinoozërsk coal deposit	coal	51 30N	106 00E	34
Guzar	ppl	38 36N	066 15E	56,RM
Gydan Peninsula	pen	70 50N	079 00E	16,RM
H				
Haapsalu	ppl	58 56N	023 33E	56,RM
Habomai Islands	isls	43 30N	146 10E	RM
Hiiumaa	isl	58 50N	022 40E	RM
I				
Igarka	ppl	67 28N	086 35E	57,59,RM
Ignalina	ppl	55 21N	026 10E	53,RM
Ignalina	nucp	NA	NA	52,53,67
Igrim	gasf	62 58N	064 13E	16
Ik	stm	55 55N	052 36E	20
Il'pyrskiy	ppl	59 56N	164 10E	RM
Ili	stm	45 24N	074 08E	RM
Imeni Poliny Osipenko	ppl	52 25N	136 29E	RM
Inderborskiy	ppl	48 33N	051 47E	56,RM
Indigirka	stm	70 48N	148 54E	RM
Ingoda	stm	51 42N	115 48E	RM
Inguri	stm	42 24N	041 33E	50,51,67
Inguri	hydp	NA	NA	50,51,67
Inta	ppl	66 05N	060 08E	56,59,RM
Inta coal deposit	coal	65 30N	059 46E	34
Inya	stm	54 59N	082 59E	60
Inza	ppl	53 51N	046 21E	RM
Iokanga	ppl	68 00N	039 41E	56,RM

Name	Feature	Latitude	Longitude	Page
I (continued)				
Iony, Ostrov	isl	56 26N	143 25E	RM
Irbit	ppl	57 41N	063 03E	RM
Iriklinskiy	ppl	51 39N	058 38E	RM
Iriklinskiy	thep	NA	NA	49,67
Irkutsk	ppl	52 16N	104 20E	32,55,57,79,RM
Irkutsk coal basin	coal	53 00N	102 30E	34,35,40
Irkutsk-10 Heat and Power	thep	NA	NA	49,67
Irkutskaya Ob ast'	admd	56 00N	106 00E	79
Irsha	ppl	55 55N	094 48E	60,RM
Irsha-Borodino coal deposit	coal	55 45N	095 13E	34,60
Irtysh	stm	61 04N	068 52E	16,50,67,RM
Isakov	oilf	64 30N	056 03E	20
Ishim	ppl	56 09N	069 27E	56,RM
Ishim	stm	57 42N	071 12E	RM
Ishimbay	ppl	53 28N	056 02E	RM
Ishimbay	oilf	53 24N	065 01E	20
Ishimbay	petr	NA	NA	31,66
Iskine	oilf	47 10N	052 38E	21
Iskitim	ppl	54 37N	083 24E	RM
Islim	gasf	35 30N	062 04E	21
Issyk-Kul', Ozero	lake	42 25N	077 15E	RM
Issyk-Kul'skaya Oblast'	admd	42 30N	078 00E	79
Istok	oilf	58 47N	057 00E	20
Istra	ppl	55 55N	036 52E	62,RM
Itatskiy	ppl	56 04N	089 05E	56,60,RM
Itatskiy coal deposit	coal	56 15N	089 00E	34,60
Iturup, Ostrov	isl	45 00N	148 00E	RM
Iul'tin	ppl	67 50N	178 48W	57,RM
Ivano-Frankovsk	ppl	48 56N	024 43E	79,RM
Ivano-Frankovskaya Oblast'	admd	48 30N	024 30E	79
Ivanovo	ppl	57 00N	040 59E	79,RM
Ivanovskaya Oblast'	admd	57 00N	042 00E	79
Ivdel'	ppl	60 42N	060 24E	RM
Iya	stm	55 33N	102 07E	60
Izberbash	oilf	42 13N	047 58E	21
Izhma	stm	65 19N	052 54E	20,RM
Izmail	ppl	45 21N	028 50E	32,56,RM
Izvestkovyy	ppl	48 59N	131 33E	RM
Izyum	ppl	49 12N	037 19E	RM
J				
Japan, Sea of	sea	43 30N	135 45E	RM
Jelgava	ppl	56 39N	023 42E	RM
Jūrmala	ppl	56 58N	023 34E	RM
K				
Kabardino-Balkarskaya ASSR	admd	43 30N	043 30E	79
Kachug	ppl	53 58N	105 52E	57,RM
Kadzhi-Say	ppl	42 08N	077 10E	RM
Kadzhi-Say uranium deposit	u/t	NA	NA	42,43
Kafan	ppl	39 12N	046 24E	RM
Kaišiadorys	ppl	54 52N	024 27E	51,56,RM
Kaišiadorys	hydp	NA	NA	50,67
Kalach-na-Donu	ppl	48 43N	043 31E	RM
Kalai-Khumb	ppl	38 28N	070 46E	56,RM
Kalamkas	oilf	45 11N	052 07E	21
Kalinin	ppl	56 52N	035 55E	56,79,RM
Kalinin	nucp	NA	NA	52,67
Kaliningrad	ppl	54 43N	020 30E	56,79,RM
Kaliningradskaya Oblast'	admd	54 45N	021 30E	79
Kalinirskaya Ob ast'	admd	57 00N	035 00E	79
Kalmykovo	ppl	49 02N	051 50E	56,59,RM
Kalmytskaya ASSR	admd	40 30N	045 30E	79
Kaluga	ppl	54 31N	036 16E	56,79,RM
Kalush	ppl	49 01N	024 22E	RM
Kaluzhskaya Oblast'	admd	54 30N	035 30E	79
Kama	stm	55 25N	050 40E	20,50,51,67,RM
Kamchatka	stm	56 15N	162 30E	RM
Kamchatka Peninsula	pen	56 00N	160 00E	64,RM
Kamchatskaya Oblast'	admd	55 00N	160 00E	79
Kamen'	ppl	53 47N	081 20E	RM
Kamen'-Rybolov	ppl	44 45N	132 04E	57,RM
Kamenets-Podol'skiy	ppl	48 40N	026 34E	RM
Kamenka	ppl	58 33N	095 51E	RM
Kamenka	oilf	65 03N	056 31E	20
Kamennoye	oilf	61 33N	067 20E	16
Kamensk-Ural'sk y	ppl	56 25N	061 56E	RM
Kamskoye Vodok ranilishche	resv	58 52N	056 15E	20
Kamyshin	ppl	50 06N	045 24E	56,RM
Kamyshldzha	oilf	38 16N	054 07E	21
Kan	stm	56 31N	093 47E	60
Kandry	oilf	54 42N	054 15E	20
Kandym	gasf	39 27N	063 31E	21,66
Kanin, Poluostrov	pen	68 00N	045 00E	RM
Kansk	ppl	56 13N	095 41E	57,60,RM
Kansk-Achinsk coal basin	coal	56 30N	093 00E	34,35,36,37,38, 40,41,60
Kansu	gasf	42 45N	054 30E	21
Kapchagay	ppl	43 50N	077 05E	RM
Kapustin Yar	ppl	48 34N	045 45E	RM
Kara Sea	sea	76 00N	080 00E	RM
Kara-Balta uranium processing center	u/t	NA	NA	42,43
Kara-Balty	ppl	42 50N	073 52E	RM
Kara-Bogaz-Gol, Zaliv	gulf	41 00N	053 15E	RM
Karaarn	oilf	46 10N	053 23E	21
Karabagly	oilf	39 22N	049 05E	21
Karabil'	gasf	36 09N	062 46E	21
Karabula	ppl	58 02N	097 23E	RM
Karabulak	oilf	43 12N	044 35E	21
Karabutak	ppl	49 59N	060 14E	56,RM
Karacha-Yelga	oilf	55 16N	055 09E	20
Karachaganak	gasf	51 16N	053 27E	20,23
Karachayevo-Cherkesskaya AO	admd	44 00N	042 00E	79
Karachop	gasf	35 20N	062 28E	21
Karadag	oilf	40 10N	049 33E	21
Karaganda	ppl	49 50N	073 10E	56,79,RM
Karaganda coal basin	coal	49 45N	073 00E	34,35,36,37,40
Karagandinskaya Oblast'	admd	48 00N	070 00E	79
Karagayly	ppl	49 22N	075 58E	56,RM
Karaginskiy, Ostrov	isl	58 50N	164 00E	RM
Karakalpakskaya ASSR	admd	43 00N	059 00E	79
Karakum	gasf	39 03N	065 35E	21
Karakum Desert	dst	39 00N	060 00E	RM
Karakumskiy Kanal	can	37 35N	065 43E	RM
Karamov	oilf	63 37N	074 37E	16
Karashaganak	ppl	51 27N	053 25E	RM
Karasuk	ppl	53 44N	078 02E	56,RM
Karatal	stm	46 26N	077 10E	RM
Karaton	oilf	46 25N	053 20E	21
Karazhal	ppl	48 02N	070 49E	56,RM
Karazhanbas	oilf	45 00N	051 35E	21

71

K (continued)

Name	Feature	Latitude	Longitude	Page
Kumertau coal deposit	coal	52 43N	055 39E	34
Kun'ya	stm	56 31N	038 12E	50,67
Kunashir, Ostrov	isl	44 10N	146 00E	RM
Kungrad	ppl	43 02N	058 49E	21,56,RM
Kungur	ppl	57 19N	056 49E	RM
Kuoyka tar sands deposit	tars	69 38N	121 22E	45
Kupino	ppl	54 22N	077 18E	RM
Kupyansk	ppl	49 42N	037 38E	RM
Kur'ya	gasf	61 46N	057 33E	20
Kura	stm	39 24N	049 19E	21,50,51,RM
Kurakhovo	ppl	47 59N	037 16E	RM
Kurakhovo	thep	NA	NA	49,67
Kureyka	stm	66 30N	087 12E	RM
Kurgan	ppl	55 26N	065 18E	56,79,RM
Kurgan-Tyube	ppl	37 50N	068 47E	79,RM
Kurgan-Tyubinskaya Oblast'	admd	37 40N	068 40E	79
Kurganskaya Oblast'	admd	55 30N	064 00E	79
Kuril Islands	isls	46 10N	152 00E	RM
Kursk	ppl	51 42N	036 12E	56,58,59,79,RM
Kursk	nucp	NA	NA	52,67
Kurskaya Oblast'	admd	51 30N	036 00E	79
Kushka	ppl	35 16N	062 20E	21,56,RM
Kushkul'	oilf	55 28N	056 13E	20
Kushmurun coal deposit	coal	52 30N	065 00E	34
Kustanay	ppl	53 10N	063 35E	55,56,79,RM
Kustanayskaya Oblast'	admd	51 00N	064 00E	79
Kutaisi	ppl	42 15N	042 40E	RM
Kuybyshev	ppl	55 27N	078 19E	RM
Kuybyshev	ppl	53 12N	050 09E	20,27,32,55,56,59,79,RM
Kuybyshevskaya Oblast'	admd	53 00N	050 00E	20,79
Kuybyshevskoye Vodokhranilishche	resv	53 40N	049 00E	20
Kuydzhik	gasf	39 03N	054 42E	21
Kuyeda	oilf	56 26N	055 33E	20
Kuzbayevo	oilf	56 03N	055 10E	20
Kuznetsk	ppl	53 07N	046 36E	RM
Kuznetsk coal basin	coal	54 30N	087 00E	34,35,36,37,38,40,41,60
Kyakhta	ppl	50 20N	106 30E	57,RM
Kyrtayel'	oilf	63 53N	054 48E	20
Kysyl-Syr	ppl	63 53N	122 46E	RM
Kyurdamir	ppl	40 21N	048 11E	56,RM
Kyurovdag	oilf	39 35N	049 04E	21
Kyursangya	oilf	39 27N	049 16E	21
Kyzyl	ppl	51 42N	094 27E	57,79,RM
Kyzyl coal deposit	coal	51 28N	094 44E	34
Kyzyl-Dzhar uranium deposit	u/t	NA	NA	42,43
Kyzyl-Kiya coal deposit	coal	40 16N	072 15E	34
Kyzyl'kum	gasf	39 11N	054 32E	21
Kyzylkum Desert	dst	42 00N	064 00E	RM
Kyzyltal coal deposit	coal	51 30N	065 30E	34
Kzyl-Orda	ppl	44 48N	065 28E	56,79,RM
Kzyl-Ordinskaya Oblast'	admd	45 00N	065 00E	79

L

Name	Feature	Latitude	Longitude	Page
L'vov	ppl	49 50N	024 00E	55,56,79,RM
L'vov	petr	NA	NA	31,66
L'vov-Volyn' coal basin	coal	50 30N	024 30E	34
L'vovskaya Oblast'	admd	50 00N	024 00E	79
La Perouse Strait	strt	45 45N	142 00E	RM
Labytnangi	ppl	66 39N	066 21E	16,17,18,RM
Ladoga, Lake	lake	61 00N	031 30E	RM
Ladyzhin	ppl	48 40N	029 15E	RM
Ladyzhin	thep	NA	NA	49,67
Lagodekhi	ppl	41 49N	046 16E	56,RM
Lake Onega uranium deposit	u/t	NA	NA	42,43
Lam	gasf	39 12N	052 31E	21
Langepas	ppl	61 13N	075 17E	16,RM
Laptev Sea	sea	76 00N	126 00E	RM
Latvian SSR	admd	57 00N	025 00E	79
Layavozh	gasf	67 44N	054 51E	20,66
Lazarev	ppl	52 13N	142 32E	RM
Ledovoye	oilf	59 51N	076 54E	16
Lem"yu	oilf	64 15N	055 22E	20
Lem'ya	oilf	60 57N	063 12E	16
Lena	stm	72 25N	126 40E	RM
Lena coal basin	coal	63 00N	123 00E	34,35,40
Lena Plateau	upld	60 45N	125 00E	RM
Lena-Tunguska oil and gas region	reg	58 00N	107 00E	14,25,32
Leninabad	ppl	40 17N	069 37E	79,RM
Leninabadskaya Oblast'	admd	40 00N	069 10E	79
Leninakan	ppl	40 48N	043 50E	56,RM
Leningrad	ppl	59 55N	030 15E	32,55,56,59,79,RM
Leningrad	nucp	NA	NA	52,53,67
Leningrad oil shale field	oils	59 01N	029 11E	44
Leningradskaya Oblast'	admd	60 00N	032 00E	79
Leninogorsk	ppl	54 36N	052 30E	RM
Leninogorsk	ppl	50 22N	083 32E	56,RM
Leninsk (Tyuratam)	ppl	45 40N	063 20E	56,RM
Leninsk-Kuznetskiy	ppl	54 38N	086 10E	60,RM
Leninsk-Kuznetskiy coal deposit	coal	54 45N	086 00E	34
Leninskoye	ppl	47 56N	132 38E	57,RM
Lensk	ppl	60 43N	114 55E	57,58,59,RM
Lermontov	ppl	44 06N	042 57E	RM
Lermontov uranium deposit/processing center	u/t	NA	NA	42,43
Lesosibirsk	ppl	58 20N	092 20E	57,60,RM
Lesozavodsk	ppl	45 28N	133 27E	57,RM
Lida	ppl	53 53N	025 18E	RM
Liepāja	ppl	56 31N	021 01E	56,RM
Lipetsk	ppl	52 37N	039 35E	56,79,RM
Lipetskaya Oblast'	admd	52 30N	039 00E	79
Lisakovsk	ppl	52 39N	062 45E	56,RM
Lisichansk	ppl	48 55N	038 26E	RM
Lisichansk	petr	NA	NA	31,66
Listvenka	oilf	57 08N	053 36E	20
Listvyanka	ppl	51 52N	104 51E	RM
Lithuanian	thep	NA	NA	49,67
Lithuanian SSR	admd	56 00N	024 00E	79
Little BAM	rr	56 30N	124 50E	11
Livanov	gasf	39 41N	051 58E	21
Lobanovo	oilf	57 45N	056 13E	20
Lodeynoye Pole	ppl	60 44N	033 33E	56,RM
Lokosovo	oilf	61 11N	075 06E	16
Lomovoye	oilf	59 34N	077 09E	16
Longa, Proliv	strt	70 20N	178 00E	RM
Lovozero	ppl	68 00N	035 00E	RM
Lovozero Tundra uranium/thorium deposit	u/t	NA	NA	42,43
Lower Kama	hydp	NA	NA	50,67
Lower Kama-1 Heat and Power	thep	NA	NA	49,67
Luchegorsk	ppl	46 29N	134 12E	57,RM
Luga	ppl	58 44N	029 52E	RM

L (continued)

Name	Feature	Latitude	Longitude	Page
Lugovoy	ppl	42 56N	072 45E	RM
Lukoml'	ppl	54 42N	029 09E	RM
Lukoml'	thep	NA	NA	48,49,67
Lumbovskiy Zaliv	gulf	67 48N	040 27E	63
Lutsk	ppl	50 45N	025 20E	56,79,RM
Luza	ppl	60 39N	047 10E	56,RM
Luza	oilf	65 00N	055 33E	20
Lyantor	oilf	61 36N	072 01E	16

M

Name	Feature	Latitude	Longitude	Page
Magadan	ppl	59 34N	150 48E	57,59,79,RM
Magadanskaya Oblast'	admd	65 00N	160 00E	79
Magnitogorsk	ppl	53 27N	059 04E	56,RM
Mago	ppl	53 15N	140 13E	RM
Makarikha	oilf	66 34N	058 17E	20
Makarov coal region	coal	49 00N	143 00E	34
Makat	ppl	47 39N	053 19E	21,RM
Makeyevka	ppl	48 02N	037 53E	RM
Makhachkala	ppl	42 58N	047 30E	56,79,RM
Makhachkala	gasf	42 46N	047 31E	21
Makinsk	ppl	52 37N	070 26E	56,RM
Makushino	ppl	55 13N	067 13E	56,RM
Malgobek	oilf	43 24N	044 37E	21
Malochernogorsk	oilf	61 10N	077 17E	16
Malorechensk	oilf	60 33N	077 08E	16
Maloyamal	gasf	68 20N	071 49E	16
Mama	ppl	58 18N	112 54E	57,RM
Mamakan	ppl	57 48N	114 01E	57,59,RM
Mamontovo	ppl	60 46N	072 47E	16,17,RM
Mamontovo	oilf	60 39N	072 37E	16,22,66
Mana	stm	55 57N	092 28E	60
Mancharovo	oilf	55 24N	054 28E	20
Mangut	ppl	49 42N	112 40E	RM
Mangyshlak Peninsula	pen	44 18N	051 00E	21,RM
Mangyshlakskaya Oblast'	admd	44 00N	054 00E	79
Manzurka	ppl	53 30N	106 04E	RM
Margilan	ppl	40 27N	071 42E	RM
Mariyskaya ASSR	admd	56 30N	048 00E	79
Markha	stm	63 28N	118 50E	RM
Markovo	ppl	64 40N	170 25E	RM
Martyshi	oilf	47 11N	050 44E	21
Mary	ppl	37 36N	061 50E	21,32,55,56,79,RM
Mary	thep	NA	NA	48,49,67
Maryyskaya Oblast'	admd	37 00N	062 30E	79
Matyushkin	oilf	60 08N	076 57E	16
Maya	stm	60 24N	134 30E	RM
Mayak	oilf	57 25N	055 40E	20
Maykop	ppl	44 35N	040 10E	56,RM
Maykop	oilf	59 00N	055 58E	20
Maykuben coal deposit	coal	50 45N	076 00E	34
Mayna	ppl	53 00N	091 28E	RM
Mayskoye	gasf	37 20N	062 05E	21
Mažeikiai	ppl	56 19N	022 20E	RM
Mažeikiai	petr	NA	NA	31,66
Medvezh'i Ostrova	isls	70 52N	161 26E	RM
Medvezh'ye	gasf	66 08N	074 09E	15,16,17,18,23,32,66
Megion	ppl	61 03N	076 06E	16,17,19,RM
Megion	oilf	60 58N	076 20E	16,66
Melitopol'	ppl	46 50N	035 22E	RM
Messoyakha	gasf	68 59N	082 58E	16,32,59
Mezen'	ppl	65 50N	044 16E	RM
Mezen'	stm	66 11N	043 59E	20,RM
Mezenskaya Guba	bay	66 40N	043 45E	63
Mezhdurechensk	ppl	53 42N	088 03E	RM
Mezhdurechenskiy	ppl	59 36N	065 56E	16,RM
Miass	ppl	54 59N	060 06E	RM
Michayu	oilf	64 00N	055 47E	20
Michurinsk	ppl	52 54N	040 30E	56,RM
Middle Olenëk tar sands deposit	tars	68 12N	121 15E	45
Middle Volga power system	reg	54 00N	048 00E	46,55
Mikhaylovka	ppl	50 04N	043 15E	RM
Mikhaylovskiy	ppl	51 49N	079 45E	RM
Mikun'	ppl	62 21N	050 06E	56,RM
Min-Kush	ppl	41 41N	074 28E	RM
Min-Kush uranium deposit/processing center	u/t	NA	NA	42,43
Mingechaur	ppl	40 45N	047 03E	RM
Minsk	ppl	53 54N	027 34E	53,55,56,79,RM
Minsk ATETs	nucp	NA	NA	52,67
Minskaya Oblast'	admd	54 00N	028 00E	79
Minusinsk	ppl	53 43N	091 42E	RM
Minusinsk coal basin	coal	53 30N	091 15E	34
Mirbashir	oilf	40 12N	046 52E	21
Mirnyy	ppl	62 33N	113 53E	57,58,59,RM
Mirzaani	oilf	41 19N	046 05E	21
Mishkino	oilf	57 08N	054 03E	20
Mishovdag	oilf	39 48N	049 11E	21
Modar	gasf	39 24N	057 55E	21
Mogilëv	ppl	53 54N	030 21E	56,79,RM
Mogilëvskaya Oblast'	admd	54 00N	030 45E	79
Mogoyto	ppl	54 25N	110 27E	RM
Moldavian	thep	NA	NA	49,67
Moldavian SSR	admd	47 00N	029 00E	79
Mollaker	gasf	37 05N	061 20E	21
Molodechno	ppl	54 19N	026 51E	RM
Monchegorsk	ppl	67 56N	032 58E	RM
Mondy	ppl	51 40N	100 59E	RM
Mordovskaya ASSR	admd	54 30N	044 00E	79
Morozovsk	ppl	48 22N	041 51E	56,RM
Morshansk	ppl	53 26N	041 49E	RM
Mortym'ya-Teterev	oilf	60 33N	064 38E	16
Moscow	ppl	55 45N	037 35E	32,55,56,59,79,RM
Moscow coal basin	coal	54 30N	036 00E	34,35,36,37,40
Moskal'vo	ppl	53 35N	142 30E	11,RM
Moskovskaya Oblast'	admd	55 45N	037 30E	79
Moskva	stm	55 05N	038 51E	RM
Moskva (Moscow) Lyubertsy	petr	NA	NA	31,66
Moyynty	ppl	47 14N	073 20E	RM
Mozdok	ppl	43 44N	044 40E	56,RM
Mozyr'	ppl	52 03N	029 16E	RM
Mozyr'	petr	NA	NA	31,66
Mubarek	ppl	39 16N	065 10E	21,RM
Mubarek	gasf	39 21N	065 28E	21
Mugun coal deposit	coal	54 00N	100 30E	34
Mukachevo	ppl	48 27N	022 43E	56,64,RM
Mukhanovo	oilf	53 21N	051 24E	20,66
Multanovo	oilf	60 06N	073 14E	16
Mulym'ya	oilf	60 15N	064 37E	16
Muna	stm	67 52N	123 06E	RM
Muna tar sands deposit	tars	67 07N	122 27E	45
Munalyk	oilf	46 45N	054 49E	21

Name	Feature	Latitude	Longitude	Page
M (continued)				
Muradkhanly	oilf	39 46N	047 51E	21
Murgab	stm	38 18N	061 12E	RM
Murmansk	ppl	68 58N	033 05E	55,56,59,79,RM
Murmanskaya Oblast'	admd	68 00N	034 00E	79
Murom	ppl	55 34N	042 02E	RM
Musina	oilf	53 04N	055 45E	20
Mutnovskaya Sopka	volc	52 27N	158 11E	64,RM
Muyunkum Desert	dst	44 30N	070 00E	RM
Mys Shmidta	ppl	68 56N	179 27W	RM
Mysovoye	ppl	45 27N	035 50E	62,RM
N				
Nadvornaya	ppl	48 38N	024 34E	RM
Nadvornaya	petr	NA	NA	31,66,RM
Nadym	ppl	65 32N	072 32E	16,17,19,32,59,RM
Nadym	stm	66 12N	072 00E	16,19,RM
Nadym	gasf	65 36N	073 00E	16
Naftalan	oilf	40 23N	046 38E	21
Nagorno-Karabakhskaya AO	admd	40 00N	046 35E	79
Nagumanskoye	gasf	51 00N	055 02E	20
Naip	gasf	40 42N	061 31E	21,66
Nakhichevan'	ppl	39 12N	045 24E	56,79,RM
Nakhichevanskaya ASSR	admd	39 15N	045 30E	79
Nakhodka	ppl	42 48N	132 52E	57,RM
Nakhodka	gasf	68 04N	077 59E	16,66
Nal'chik	ppl	43 29N	043 37E	79,RM
Namangan	ppl	41 00N	071 40E	56,79,RM
Namanganskaya Oblast'	admd	41 00N	071 30E	79
Namtsy	ppl	62 43N	129 37E	RM
Nar'yan-Mar	ppl	67 39N	053 00E	20,RM
Narva	ppl	59 23N	028 12E	44,RM
Naryn	ppl	41 26N	075 58E	56,79,RM
Naryn	ppl	38 17N	068 55E	RM
Naryn	stm	41 08N	072 05E	50,51,67,RM
Narynkol	ppl	42 43N	080 12E	RM
Narynskaya Oblast'	admd	41 30N	075 30E	79
Natanebi tar sands deposit	tars	42 44N	042 39E	45
Naugarzan uranium deposit	u/t	NA	NA	42,43
Naushki	ppl	50 22N	106 07E	RM
Navoi	ppl	40 09N	065 22E	56,79,RM
Navoi	thep	NA	NA	49,67
Navoiyskaya Oblast'	admd	42 00N	064 30E	79
Nazarovo	ppl	56 01N	090 26E	57,60,RM
Nazarovo	thep	NA	NA	49,67
Nazarovo coal deposit	coal	55 50N	090 30E	34
Nebit-Dag	ppl	39 30N	054 22E	32,56,RM
Nebit-Dag	oilf	39 06N	054 18E	21,66
Nebit-Dag tar sands deposit	tars	40 23N	053 57E	45
Neftechala	oilf	39 06N	049 09E	21
Neftekamsk	ppl	56 05N	054 16E	RM
Neftekumsk	oilf	44 20N	044 37E	21
Nefteyugansk	ppl	61 05N	072 42E	16,17,19,RM
Neftezavodsk	petr	NA	NA	31,66
Neftyanyye Kamni	oilf	40 06N	050 43E	21,66
Nelidovo	ppl	56 13N	032 46E	56,RM
Nelidovo coal basin	coal	56 15N	033 04E	34
Neman	stm	55 18N	021 23E	50,67
Nenetskiy AOk	admd	67 30N	054 00E	20,79
Nenoksa	ppl	64 38N	039 11E	RM
Neryungri	ppl	56 41N	124 39E	11,57,59,RM
Neryungri	thep	NA	NA	11,59
Neryungri coal deposit	coal	56 40N	124 15E	11,34
Never	ppl	53 59N	124 10E	11,57,RM
Nevinnomyssk	ppl	44 38N	041 57E	RM
Nevinnomyssk	thep	NA	NA	49,67
New Siberian Islands	isls	75 00N	142 00E	RM
Neyto	gasf	70 03N	070 08E	16,66
Nezhin	ppl	51 03N	031 53E	56,RM
Nikel'	ppl	69 24N	030 12E	56,RM
Nikol'skiy	ppl	47 58N	067 33E	RM
Nikol'skoye	oilf	52 52N	053 05E	20
Nikolayev	ppl	46 58N	032 00E	56,79,RM
Nikolayevsk	ppl	53 08N	140 44E	57,RM
Nikolayevskaya Oblast'	admd	47 15N	032 00E	79
Nikolayevskoye	oilf	44 56N	041 34E	21
Nikopol'	ppl	47 34N	034 24E	RM
Nizhneangarsk	ppl	55 47N	109 33E	57,RM
Nizhnekamsk	ppl	55 36N	051 47E	RM
Nizhnekamsk	petr	NA	NA	31,66
Nizhneomra	oilf	62 38N	056 20E	20
Nizhnesortym	oilf	62 39N	070 57E	16
Nizhneudinsk	ppl	54 54N	099 03E	57,RM
Nizhnevartovsk	ppl	60 56N	076 38E	16,17,18,19,31,32,56,RM
Nizhneyansk	ppl	71 26N	136 04E	RM
Nizhniy Bestyakh	ppl	61 58N	129 56E	RM
Nizhniy Tagil	ppl	57 55N	059 57E	RM
Nizhnyaya Poyma	ppl	56 11N	097 13E	60,RM
Nizhnyaya Tunguska	stm	65 48N	088 04E	RM
Nizhnyaya Tura	ppl	58 37N	059 49E	32,RM
Noginsk	ppl	55 51N	038 27E	RM
Noginsk	ppl	64 32N	091 10E	RM
Noril'sk	ppl	69 20N	088 06E	16,32,57,58,59,RM
Noril'sk coal deposit	coal	68 45N	087 30E	34
Norio	oilf	41 57N	044 45E	21
North Caspian oil and gas region	reg	57 00N	054 00E	14,21,25,32
North Caucasus oil and gas region	reg	45 00N	045 00E	14,15,21,22,25,32
North Caucasus power system	reg	46 00N	043 00E	46,55
North Caucasus Economic Region	reg	45 00N	042 00E	79
North Kazakhstan power system	reg	50 00N	073 00E	46,55
North Siberian Lowland	pln	72 00N	104 00E	RM
Northern Economic Region	reg	64 00N	045 00E	79
Northern Hills	hlls	59 30N	049 00E	RM
Northern Lights pipeline	pipe	57 00N	035 00E	10,20
Northwest power system	reg	59 00N	031 00E	46,55
Northwest Economic Region	reg	59 00N	031 00E	79
Novaya Sibir', Ostrov	isl	75 00N	149 00E	RM
Novaya Zemlya	isls	74 00N	057 00E	RM
Novgorod	ppl	58 31N	031 17E	56,79,RM
Novgorodskaya Oblast'	admd	58 30N	032 30E	79
Novikovo	ppl	46 22N	143 22E	RM
Novo-Angren	thep	NA	NA	49,67
Novoagansk	ppl	61 57N	076 41E	16,17,RM
Novoaltaysk	ppl	53 24N	083 55E	RM
Novoasharovo	oilf	53 27N	053 15E	20
Novocheboksarsk	ppl	58 08N	047 30E	RM
Novocherkassk	ppl	47 25N	040 06E	RM
Novocherkassk	thep	NA	NA	49,67
Novogornyy	ppl	55 37N	060 47E	RM
Novogornyy uranium deposit	u/t	NA	NA	42,43

Name	Feature	Latitude	Longitude	Page
N (continued)				
Novokadeyevka	oilf	54 43N	056 24E	20
Novokazalinsk	ppl	45 50N	062 10E	RM
Novokiyevskiy Uval	ppl	51 40N	128 57E	57,RM
Novokuybyshevsk	ppl	53 07N	049 58E	RM
Novokuybyshevsk Lend Lease 3	petr	NA	NA	31,66
Novokuybyshevsk No. 2	petr	NA	NA	31,66
Novokuznetsk	ppl	53 45N	087 06E	32,55,56,RM
Novomoskovsk	ppl	54 05N	038 13E	RM
Novonikolayevskiy	ppl	50 58N	042 22E	56,RM
Novopolotsk	ppl	55 32N	028 39E	RM
Novopolotsk	petr	NA	NA	31,66
Novopskov	ppl	49 33N	039 05E	32,RM
Novorossiysk	ppl	44 43N	037 47E	32,56,62,RM
Novoshakhtinsk	ppl	47 47N	039 56E	RM
Novosibirsk	ppl	55 02N	082 55E	18,32,55,56,59,79
Novosibirskaya Oblast'	admd	55 00N	080 00E	79
Novotroitsk	ppl	51 12N	058 20E	RM
Novovolynsk coal deposit	coal	50 42N	024 13E	34
Novovoronezhskiy	ppl	51 19N	039 13E	RM
Novovoronezhskiy	nucp	NA	NA	52,67
Novoyelkhovo	oilf	54 59N	052 02E	20,66
Novyy Port	ppl	67 40N	072 52E	16,59,RM
Novyy Port	gasf	67 53N	072 21E	16,66
Novyy Urengoy	ppl	66 05N	076 42E	16,17,18,19,32,55,56,59,RM
Novyy Uzen'	ppl	43 18N	052 48E	56,RM
Noyabr'sk	ppl	63 08N	075 22E	16,17,RM
Nozhovka	oilf	57 09N	054 49E	20
Nukus	ppl	42 29N	059 38E	56,79,RM
Nurek	ppl	38 23N	069 21E	56,RM
Nurek	hydp	NA	NA	50,51,67
Nurlat	oilf	54 37N	050 54E	20
Nurmin	gasf	69 02N	071 41E	16
Nyakh	ppl	62 09N	065 27E	16,RM
Nyamed	gasf	63 16N	054 15E	20
Nyandoma	ppl	61 40N	040 12E	RM
Nyda	ppl	66 36N	072 54E	16,19,RM
Nyda	gasf	66 37N	073 49E	16,66
Nysh	ppl	51 33N	142 46E	RM
Nyukzha	stm	56 35N	121 36E	11
Nyurba	ppl	63 17N	118 20E	RM
Nyuya	stm	60 32N	116 14E	RM
O				
Ob'	stm	66 45N	069 30E	16,19,60,RM
Obninsk	ppl	55 05N	036 37E	RM
Obninsk	nucp	NA	NA	67
Obozërskiy	ppl	63 29N	040 19E	RM
Obshchiy Syrt oil shale deposit	oils	51 40N	055 53E	44
Obskaya Guba	bay	69 00N	073 00E	16,RM
Odessa	ppl	46 28N	030 44E	32,53,56,79,RM
Odessa	petr	NA	NA	31,66
Odessa ATETs	nucp	NA	NA	52,67
Odesskaya Oblast'	admd	47 00N	030 00E	79
Odoptu	oilf	53 20N	143 49E	11
Oka	stm	56 42N	031 05E	RM
Oka-Don Plain	pln	53 00N	040 30E	RM
Okarem	oilf	37 53N	053 57E	21
Okha	ppl	53 34N	142 56E	11,32,57,59,RM
Okhotsk	ppl	59 23N	143 18E	RM
Okhotsk coal area	coal	59 45N	147 00E	34
Okhotsk, Sea of	sea	55 00N	150 00E	11,RM
Oktyabr'sk	ppl	49 28N	057 25E	RM
Oktyabr'sk	ppl	53 10N	048 42E	RM
Oktyabr'skiy	ppl	52 40N	156 14E	RM
Oktyabr'skiy	ppl	39 06N	066 49E	RM
Oktyabr'skiy	ppl	54 28N	053 28E	RM
Oktyabr'skiy	ppl	53 01N	128 37E	57,RM
Oktyabr'skoy Revolyutsii, Ostrov	isl	79 30N	097 00E	RM
Oktyabr'skoye	ppl	62 28N	066 03E	RM
Ol'doy	stm	53 33N	123 21E	11
Ol'ga	ppl	43 45N	135 18E	57,RM
Ol'khovka	oilf	58 41N	056 41E	20
Olëkma	stm	60 22N	120 42E	11,RM
Olëkminsk	ppl	60 24N	120 24E	RM
Olen'ye	oilf	59 31N	076 36E	16
Olenëk	ppl	68 33N	112 18E	RM
Olenëk	stm	73 00N	119 55E	RM
Olenëk oil shale deposit	oils	67 30N	119 22E	44
Olenëk tar sands deposit	tars	71 17N	122 23E	45
Olenëkskiy Zaliv	gulf	73 20N	121 00E	RM
Oleynikov	ppl	45 31N	046 30E	21
Olovyannaya	ppl	50 56N	115 35E	RM
Oloy	stm	66 29N	159 29E	RM
Olyutorskiy Poluostrov	pen	60 15N	170 12E	RM
Omolon	stm	68 42N	158 36E	RM
Omolon coal area	coal	64 45N	159 30E	34
Omsk	ppl	55 00N	073 24E	18,32,56,79,RM
Omsk	petr	NA	NA	31,66
Omskaya Oblast'	admd	56 00N	073 00E	79
Omsukchan	ppl	62 32N	155 48E	57,59,RM
Omsukchan coal deposit	coal	62 30N	156 15E	34
Onega	ppl	63 54N	038 08E	RM
Onega, Lake	lake	61 30N	035 45E	RM
Onon	stm	51 42N	115 50E	RM
Opukha coal area	coal	62 00N	173 30E	34
Or'ya	oilf	56 06N	054 44E	20
Ordzhonikidze	ppl	43 00N	044 40E	21,56,79,RM
Orël	ppl	52 55N	036 05E	56,79,RM
Orenburg	ppl	51 45N	055 06E	10,20,32,55,56,79,RM
Orenburg	gasf	51 45N	054 47E	15,20,23,66
Orenburgskaya Oblast'	admd	52 00N	056 00E	20,79
Orlovskaya Oblast'	admd	53 00N	036 15E	79
Orsha	ppl	54 31N	030 26E	RM
Orsk	ppl	51 12N	058 34E	32,56,RM
Orsk	petr	NA	NA	31,66
Orsk 421	petr	NA	NA	31,66
Osa	oilf	57 14N	055 25E	20
Osh	ppl	40 32N	072 48E	56,79,RM
Osh coal deposit	coal	40 30N	073 00E	34
Oshmarino	ppl	71 47N	082 50E	RM
Oshskaya Oblast'	admd	40 00N	073 00E	79
Osinniki	ppl	53 37N	087 21E	RM
Ostrov Bulla	oilf	40 04N	049 37E	21,66
Oymyakon	ppl	63 28N	142 49E	RM
Ozek-Suat	oilf	44 29N	044 47E	21
Ozërnyy	gasf	70 29N	085 06E	16

Name	Feature	Latitude	Longitude	Page

P

Name	Feature	Latitude	Longitude	Page
Pakhachi	ppl	60 34N	169 03E	RM
Pal'yanovo	oilf	61 50N	066 41E	16
Palana	ppl	59 07N	159 58E	RM
Palatka	ppl	60 06N	150 54E	57,RM
Palyavaam	stm	68 50N	170 45E	RM
Pamirs	mts	38 00N	073 00E	RM
Panevėžys	ppl	55 44N	024 21E	RM
Panfilov	ppl	44 10N	080 01E	56,RM
Pangody	ppl	65 51N	074 30E	16,17,RM
Paramushir, Ostrov	isl	50 25N	155 50E	RM
Paratunka	ppl	52 57N	158 14E	57,64,RM
Pärnu	ppl	58 24N	024 32E	56,RM
Paromay	ppl	52 50N	143 02E	57,RM
Partizansk	ppl	43 07N	133 05E	RM
Partizansk coal basin	coal	43 15N	133 00E	34
Pashnya	oilf	63 16N	056 20E	20
Patara	oilf	41 09N	046 26E	21
Pauzhetka	ppl	51 28N	156 48E	57,64,RM
Pavlodar	ppl	52 18N	076 57E	32,56,59,79,RM
Pavlodar	petr	NA	NA	31,66
Pavlodarskaya Oblast'	admd	52 00N	076 00E	79
Pavlograd	ppl	47 00N	035 03E	RM
Pavlovskoye	ppl	56 34N	056 06E	20
Pechenga	ppl	69 33N	031 12E	RM
Pechora	ppl	65 25N	057 02E	20,32,56,59,RM
Pechora	stm	68 13N	054 15E	20,50,51,RM
Pechora coal basin	coal	67 00N	062 00E	34,35,36,37,39,40
Pechora-Kozhva	gasf	65 15N	056 58E	20
Pechorskoye More	sea	70 00N	054 00E	RM
Peipus, Lake	lake	58 45N	027 30E	RM
Pelyatka	gasf	69 44N	081 53E	16,66
Peno	ppl	56 55N	032 45E	RM
Penza	ppl	53 13N	045 00E	56,79,RM
Penzenskaya Oblast'	admd	53 00N	044 30E	79
Penzhina	stm	62 28N	165 18E	RM
Penzhinskaya Guba	bay	61 00N	162 00E	63,RM
Peregrebnoye	ppl	62 58N	065 05E	RM
Perm'	ppl	58 00N	056 15E	20,32,56,79,RM
Perm'	thep	NA	NA	49,67
Perm'	petr	NA	NA	31,66
Permskaya Oblast'	admd	59 00N	056 00E	20,79
Permyakov	oilf	61 27N	079 30E	16
Pervomaysk	ppl	48 03N	030 52E	RM
Pervomaysk	ppl	46 26N	141 57E	RM
Pervomayskoye	oilf	59 09N	076 14E	16
Pervoural'sk	ppl	56 54N	059 58E	RM
Pestsovyy	gasf	67 02N	075 21E	16,66
Petropavlovsk	ppl	54 52N	069 06E	56,79,RM
Petropavlovsk-Kamchatskiy	ppl	53 01N	158 39E	57,59,79,RM
Petrovsk	ppl	52 19N	045 23E	32,RM
Petrovsk-Zabaykal'skiy	ppl	51 17N	108 50E	57,RM
Petrozavodsk	ppl	61 49N	034 20E	56,79,RM
Pevek	ppl	69 42N	170 17E	57,59,RM
Pikhtovka	ppl	56 00N	082 42E	RM
Pilyugino	oilf	53 23N	052 18E	20
Pinega	stm	64 08N	041 54E	RM
Pinsk	ppl	52 07N	026 07E	56,RM
Pionerskoye iron ore deposit	iron	57 30N	125 05E	11
Plesetsk	ppl	62 43N	040 17E	RM
Pobedino	ppl	49 51N	142 49E	RM
Podkamennaya Tunguska	ppl	61 36N	090 09E	RM
Podkamennaya Tunguska	stm	61 36N	090 18E	RM
Pogranichnyy	ppl	44 25N	131 24E	RM
Pokachi	oilf	61 42N	074 59E	16,66
Pokosnyy	ppl	55 31N	101 04E	57,RM
Pokrovka	oilf	52 49N	049 39E	20
Pokrovka	oilf	53 01N	052 47E	20
Pokrovsk	ppl	61 29N	129 06E	57,RM
Polazna	oilf	58 15N	056 25E	20
Poles'ye	reg	52 00N	027 00E	RM
Polevskoy	ppl	56 26N	060 11E	RM
Polotsk	ppl	55 29N	028 47E	32,56,RM
Poltava	ppl	49 35N	034 34E	79,RM
Poltavskaya Oblast'	admd	49 30N	034 00E	79
Poludennoye	ppl	60 07N	078 09E	16
Polyarnyy	ppl	69 38N	178 44E	59,RM
Pomary	ppl	55 58N	048 21E	10,20,RM
Ponomarevka	oilf	53 18N	054 04E	20
Ponoy	stm	66 59N	041 17E	RM
Popigay	stm	72 54N	106 36E	RM
Poronaysk	ppl	49 13N	143 07E	57,RM
Pos'yet	ppl	42 39N	130 48E	RM
Potanay	oilf	61 15N	065 56E	16
Poti	ppl	42 09N	041 40E	RM
Povkh	oilf	62 28N	075 51E	16
Poyarkovo	ppl	49 36N	128 41E	RM
Pravdinsk	oilf	60 51N	071 47E	16,29,66
Pravobereg	gasf	62 13N	056 38E	20
Priargunsk	ppl	50 24N	119 06E	57,RM
Pridneprovsk	ppl	48 24N	035 07E	RM
Pridneprovsk	thep	NA	NA	49,67
Priluki	ppl	50 36N	032 24E	RM
Primorskiy Kray	admd	45 00N	135 00E	79
Primorsko-Akhtarsk	ppl	46 03N	038 10E	RM
Pripyat'	stm	51 10N	030 30E	RM
Prokop'yevsk	ppl	53 53N	086 45E	RM
Prokop'yevsk coal deposit	coal	54 15N	086 45E	34
Promyshlenyy	oilf	67 35N	063 55E	RM
Pron'kino	oilf	52 47N	052 34E	20
Prorva	oilf	45 51N	053 20E	21
Provideniya	ppl	64 23N	173 18W	RM
Przheval'sk	ppl	42 29N	078 24E	56,79,RM
Pskov	ppl	57 50N	028 20E	56,79,RM
Pskovskaya Oblast'	admd	57 30N	029 00E	79
Pugachëv	ppl	52 02N	048 49E	RM
Punga	gasf	62 40N	064 11E	16
Pur	stm	67 31N	077 55E	16,19,RM
Pushkino	ppl	51 14N	046 59E	RM
Pyasina	stm	73 50N	087 10E	16,RM
Pyatigorsk	ppl	44 01N	043 05E	56,RM
Pyt'-Yakh	ppl	60 45N	072 50E	16,17,RM

R

Name	Feature	Latitude	Longitude	Page
Radayevka	oilf	53 52N	050 57E	20
Raduzhnyy	ppl	62 06N	077 31E	16,17,RM
Rassokha	gasf	61 52N	057 19E	20
Raychikhinsk coal basin	coal	51 30N	128 00E	34,40
Razdan	ppl	40 29N	044 46E	RM
Razdan	thep	NA	NA	49,67
Razgort	ppl	63 29N	048 42E	56,RM
Razdan	ppl	52 22N	030 23E	RM
Rechitsa	ppl	52 22N	030 23E	RM
Reftinskiy	ppl	57 00N	061 30E	RM

R (continued)

Name	Feature	Latitude	Longitude	Page
Reftinskiy	thep	NA	NA	47,49,67
Revda	ppl	56 48N	059 57E	RM
Riga	ppl	56 57N	024 06E	32,56,79,RM
Riga, Gulf of	gulf	57 30N	023 35E	RM
Rogun	ppl	38 47N	069 52E	RM
Rogun	hydp	NA	NA	50,51,67
Romanovka	ppl	53 14N	112 46E	RM
Romashkino	oilf	54 50N	052 32E	17,20,22,66
Romny	ppl	50 45N	033 28E	RM
Roslavl'	ppl	53 57N	032 52E	RM
Rossokha tar sands deposit	tars	71 07N	111 02E	45
Rossosh'	ppl	50 12N	038 26E	RM
Rostov	ppl	57 11N	039 25E	55,56,59,79,RM
Rostov	nucp	NA	NA	52,67
Rostovskaya Oblast'	admd	47 00N	042 00E	79
Rovenskaya Oblast'	admd	51 00N	026 30E	79
Rovno	ppl	50 37N	026 15E	56,79,RM
Rovno	nucp	NA	NA	52,67
Rtishchevo	ppl	52 15N	043 47E	RM
Rubtsovsk	ppl	51 30N	081 15E	55,56,RM
Rudnichnyy	ppl	59 38N	052 26E	56,RM
Rudnyy	ppl	52 57N	063 07E	RM
Russian Soviet Federated Socialist Republic	admd	60 00N	100 00E	79
Russkaya	gasf	66 40N	080 33E	16,66
Russkaya tar sands deposit	tars	66 56N	080 45E	45
Russkiy Khutor	oilf	44 15N	045 19E	21
Rustavi	ppl	41 33N	045 03E	RM
Ruzayevka	ppl	54 04N	044 56E	56,RM
Ryazan'	ppl	54 38N	039 44E	56,65,79,RM
Ryazan'	thep	NA	NA	49,67
Ryazan'	petr	NA	NA	31,66
Ryazanskaya Oblast'	admd	54 15N	040 30E	79
Rybach'ye	ppl	42 26N	076 12E	56,RM
Rybinskoye Vodokhranilishche	resv	58 30N	038 25E	RM
Ryrkaypiy	ppl	68 56N	179 26W	59,RM
Rzhev	ppl	56 15N	034 20E	56,RM

S

Name	Feature	Latitude	Longitude	Page
Saaremaa	isl	58 25N	022 30E	RM
Safonovo	ppl	55 09N	033 13E	56,RM
Safonovo coal deposit	coal	55 15N	033 09E	34
Sagiz	oilf	47 26N	053 21E	21
Sakar	gasf	38 54N	063 35E	21,66
Sakhalin	isl	51 00N	143 00E	11,RM
Sakhalin oil and gas region	reg	52 00N	143 00E	11,14,25,32
Sakhalin tar sands deposit	tars	53 58N	142 47E	45
Sakhalinskaya Oblast'	admd	52 00N	142 30E	79
Sakmara	stm	51 46N	055 01E	20
Sal'sk	ppl	46 28N	041 33E	56,RM
Salaush	oilf	55 59N	052 57E	20
Salavat	ppl	53 21N	055 55E	20,RM
Salavat	petr	NA	NA	31,66
Salekhard	ppl	66 33N	066 40E	16,RM
Salym	oilf	60 47N	071 12E	16
Salyukino	oilf	66 52N	058 43E	20
Samantepe	gasf	38 59N	063 53E	21,66
Samara	stm	53 10N	050 04E	20
Samarkand	ppl	39 40N	066 58E	56,79,RM
Samarkandskaya Oblast'	admd	40 00N	067 00E	79
Samgori	oilf	41 34N	045 09E	21,66
Samotlor	oilf	61 14N	076 39E	16,17,19,22,29,66
Sangar coal deposit	coal	64 30N	128 00E	34
Sannikova, Proliv	strt	74 30N	140 00E	RM
Saran'	ppl	49 46N	072 52E	RM
Saransk	ppl	54 11N	045 11E	79,RM
Sarapul	ppl	56 28N	053 48E	RM
Saratov	ppl	51 34N	046 02E	32,56,79,RM
Saratov	hydp	NA	NA	50,67
Saratov	petr	NA	NA	31,66
Saratovskaya Oblast'	admd	51 30N	047 00E	20,79
Sarny	ppl	51 20N	026 36E	56,RM
Sartang	stm	67 44N	133 12E	RM
Sary-Ozek	ppl	44 22N	077 59E	56,RM
Saryshagan	ppl	46 06N	073 36E	56,RM
Sasovo	ppl	54 20N	041 55E	56,RM
Savuy	oilf	61 54N	073 42E	16
Sayak	ppl	47 00N	077 24E	56,RM
Sayan Mountains	mts	52 45N	096 00E	RM
Sayan-Shushenskoye	hydp	NA	NA	46,47,50,51,67
Sayanogorsk	ppl	53 05N	091 25E	55,57,RM
Saygat	oilf	61 22N	072 09E	16
Segezha	ppl	63 44N	034 19E	56,RM
Selemdzha	stm	51 42N	128 53E	RM
Semakov	gasf	69 11N	076 02E	16,66
Semenovka	oilf	53 41N	050 34E	20
Semipalatinsk	ppl	50 28N	080 13E	56,79,RM
Semipalatinskaya Oblast'	admd	49 00N	080 00E	79
Serafimovskiy	oilf	54 33N	053 35E	20
Serdobsk	ppl	52 28N	044 13E	RM
Sergeyevka	ppl	53 51N	067 25E	56,RM
Sergeyevka	oilf	54 50N	055 41E	20
Sergino	ppl	62 30N	065 38E	16,17,18,RM
Serov	ppl	59 36N	060 35E	56,RM
Serpukhov	ppl	54 55N	037 25E	RM
Sevan, Ozero	lake	40 20N	045 20E	RM
Sevastopol'	ppl	44 36N	033 32E	56,RM
Severnaya Dvina	stm	64 32N	040 30E	RM
Severnaya Sos'va	stm	64 11N	065 27E	16,RM
Severnaya Zemlya	isls	79 30N	098 00E	RM
Severnyy Pokur	oilf	60 48N	078 27E	16,66
Severo-Achak	gasf	41 06N	061 38E	21
Severo-Balkui	gasf	39 55N	061 36E	21
Severo-Buzachi	oilf	45 09N	051 50E	21
Severo-Gugurtli	gasf	40 25N	062 01E	21
Severo-Kamsk	oilf	58 07N	056 08E	20
Severo-Kazakhstarskaya Oblast'	admd	54 30N	069 00E	79
Severo-Komsomol	gasf	64 46N	076 08E	16,66
Severo-Mylva	oilf	62 17N	055 59E	20
Severo-Naip	gasf	40 42N	061 48E	21
Severo-Osetinskaya ASSR	admd	43 00N	044 00E	79
Severo-Pokur	oilf	61 12N	075 48E	16
Severo-Urengoy	gasf	67 34N	076 32E	16,66
Severo-Var'yegan	oilf	62 26N	077 25E	16,66
Severobaykal'sk	ppl	55 38N	109 19E	RM
Severodvinsk	ppl	64 34N	039 50E	56,RM
Severomorsk	ppl	69 05N	033 27E	RM
Severoural'sk	ppl	60 09N	059 57E	RM
Seymchan	ppl	62 53N	152 26E	RM
Seyrab	gasf	38 40N	062 40E	21
Shadrinsk	ppl	56 05N	063 38E	RM
Shaim	ppl	60 21N	064 10E	16,RM
Shakhpakhty	gasf	42 49N	057 22E	21

Name	Feature	Latitude	Longitude	Page
V (continued)				
Votkinsk	ppl	57 03N	053 59E	56,RM
Votkinsk	hydp	NA	NA	50,67
Voyvozh	ppl	64 21N	055 06E	RM
Vozey	oilf	66 42N	056 47E	20,66
Vuktyl	ppl	63 40N	057 20E	59,RM
Vuktyl	gasf	63 49N	057 18E	15,20,23,66
Vyatka	stm	55 36N	051 30E	20,RM
Vyaz'ma	ppl	55 13N	034 18E	RM
Vyborg	ppl	60 42N	028 45E	25,RM
Vychegda	stm	61 18N	046 36E	20,RM
Vyksa	ppl	55 18N	042 11E	33,RM
Vym'	stm	62 13N	050 25E	20
Vyngapur	gasf	63 10N	076 46E	16,23,66
Vyshniy Volochek	ppl	57 35N	034 34E	RM
Vytegra	ppl	61 00N	036 27E	56,RM
W				
West Kamchatka coal area	coal	57 30N	157 30E	34
West Siberia oil and gas region	reg	64 00N	075 00E	14,15,16,17,18, 19,22,23,25,32,33
West Siberia Economic Region	reg	60 00N	076 00E	79
West Siberian Plain	pln	60 00N	075 00E	RM
White Sea	sea	65 30N	038 00E	RM
Wrangel Island	isl	71 00N	179 30W	RM
Y				
Yablonovyy Range	mts	53 30N	115 00E	RM
Yagodnoye	ppl	62 33N	149 40E	57,RM
Yagtydin	oilf	62 38N	056 18E	20
Yakushkino	oilf	53 54N	051 31E	20
Yakutsk	ppl	62 00N	129 40E	32,57,58,59,79, RM
Yakutskaya ASSR	admd	65 00N	130 00E	79
Yalta	ppl	44 30N	034 10E	56,62,RM
Yamal Peninsula	pen	70 00N	070 00E	16,17,RM
Yamalo-Nenetskiy AOk	admd	66 00N	076 00E	17,79
Yamarovka	ppl	50 38N	110 16E	RM
Yamashi	oilf	55 05N	051 47E	20
Yamburg	gasf	68 06N	076 18E	15,16,17,23,66
Yamsovey	gasf	65 30N	075 56E	16,66
Yana	stm	71 31N	136 32E	RM
Yangikazgan	gasf	40 38N	062 37E	21
Yangiyul'	ppl	41 06N	069 03E	RM
Yanskiy Zaliv	gulf	71 50N	136 00E	RM
Yaransk	ppl	57 19N	047 54E	RM
Yarayner	oilf	63 09N	077 48E	16
Yarega	ppl	63 24N	053 28E	20
Yarega tar sands deposit	tars	65 43N	056 41E	45
Yareyyu	gasf	67 59N	055 15E	20
Yarino	oilf	58 26N	056 31E	20
Yarkino	ppl	59 08N	099 23E	RM
Yaroslavl'	ppl	57 37N	039 52E	56,79,RM
Yaroslavl'	petr	NA	NA	31,66
Yaroslavskaya Oblast'	admd	58 00N	039 30E	79
Yasnogorsk	ppl	50 51N	115 45E	57,RM
Yaun-Lor	oilf	61 27N	072 43E	16
Yefremov	ppl	53 09N	038 07E	RM
Yegindybulak	ppl	49 45N	076 23E	56,RM
Yelets	ppl	52 37N	038 30E	32,RM
Yelizarovo	oilf	61 27N	067 42E	16
Yelizovo	ppl	53 11N	158 23E	57,RM
Yelkino	oilf	57 37N	056 56E	20
Yem-Yegov	oilf	61 58N	066 06E	16
Yenisey	stm	71 50N	082 40E	16,50,51,60,67, RM
Yeniseysk	ppl	58 27N	092 10E	57,RM
Yenoruskino	oilf	54 56N	050 45E	20
Yeraliyev	ppl	43 12N	051 39E	56,RM
Yerevan	ppl	40 11N	044 30E	56,79,RM
Yergach	oilf	57 23N	056 39E	20
Yermak	ppl	52 02N	076 55E	RM
Yermak	oilf	60 47N	076 10E	16
Yermak	thep	NA	NA	49,67
Yermakovo	ppl	66 37N	086 13E	RM
Yermentau	ppl	51 38N	073 10E	RM
Yesil'	ppl	51 28N	066 24E	56,RM
Yetypur	gasf	64 01N	077 42E	16,66
Yevpatoriya	ppl	45 12N	033 22E	56,RM
Yevreyskaya AO	admd	48 30N	132 00E	79
Yeysk	ppl	46 42N	038 17E	RM
Yoshkar-Ola	ppl	56 40N	047 55E	79,RM
Yubileynyy	gasf	66 05N	075 56E	16,66
Yugo-Osetinskaya AO	admd	42 20N	044 00E	79
Yugomash	oilf	56 16N	055 31E	20
Yugorsk	oilf	61 37N	077 27E	16
Yurga	ppl	55 42N	084 51E	RM
Yurkharov	gasf	67 47N	077 19E	16
Yushkozero	ppl	64 45N	032 07E	RM
Yuzhno-Balyk	oilf	60 29N	072 28E	16
Yuzhno-Myl'dzhino	oilf	58 45N	078 05E	16
Yuzhno-Russkaya	gasf	66 04N	080 36E	16,66
Yuzhno-Sakhalinsk	ppl	46 57N	142 44E	11,57,59,79,RM
Yuzhno-Shapkina	oilf	67 11N	054 25E	20
Yuzhno-Sukhokumskoye	oilf	44 30N	045 13E	21,66
Yuzhno-Surgut	oilf	61 08N	072 57E	16
Yuzhno-Tambey	gasf	71 37N	071 57E	16,66
Yuzhno-Ural'sk	ppl	54 26N	061 15E	RM
Yuzhno-Ural'sk	thep	NA	NA	49,67
Yuzhno-Zhetybay	gasf	43 15N	052 09E	21
Yuzhnyy Bug	stm	46 59N	031 58E	50,51

Name	Feature	Latitude	Longitude	Page
Z				
Zabaykal'sk	ppl	49 38N	117 19E	RM
Zagorsk	ppl	56 18N	038 08E	51,56,RM
Zagorsk	hydp	NA	NA	50,67
Zainsk	ppl	55 18N	052 04E	56,RM
Zainsk	thep	NA	NA	49,67
Zakamensk	ppl	50 23N	103 17E	57,RM
Zakarpatskaya Oblast'	admd	48 20N	023 00E	79
Zamankul	oilf	43 18N	044 20E	21
Zapadno-Erdekli	gasf	38 44N	053 33E	21
Zapadno-Izkos'gora	gasf	62 55N	054 41E	20
Zapadno-Soplesk	gasf	64 17N	057 14E	20
Zapadno-Surgut	oilf	61 22N	073 04E	16
Zapadno-Tarkosale	gasf	64 47N	077 49E	16,66
Zapadnyy Tebuk	oilf	63 42N	054 54E	20
Zapolyarnoye	gasf	66 55N	079 14E	15,16,17,23,66
Zaporozh'ye	ppl	47 53N	035 05E	79,RM
Zaporozh'ye	thep	NA	NA	47,49,67
Zaporozh'ye	nucp	NA	NA	52,67
Zaporozhskaya Oblast'	admd	47 30N	035 30E	79
Zarafshan	ppl	41 31N	064 15E	56,RM
Zavolzh'ye	ppl	56 39N	043 24E	RM
Zaysan, Ozero	lake	48 00N	084 00E	RM
Zaysan	ppl	47 28N	084 52E	RM
Zayskoye Vodokhranilishche	resv	54 25N	127 45E	11,RM
Zelenodol'sk	ppl	55 51N	048 33E	RM
Zelënyy Mys	ppl	68 48N	161 24E	57,59,RM
Zeya	ppl	53 45N	127 16E	11,55,RM
Zeya	stm	50 15N	127 35E	11,50,51,57,67, RM
Zeya	hydp	NA	NA	50,67
Zhanatala	oilf	47 10N	050 09E	21
Zhanatas	ppl	43 34N	069 45E	56,RM
Zhanazhol	oilf	48 35N	058 00E	21
Zhannetty, Ostrov	isl	76 43N	158 00E	RM
Zharyk	ppl	48 52N	072 51E	RM
Zhdanov	ppl	47 06N	037 33E	RM
Zhdanov	gasf	39 16N	052 58E	21
Zheleznodorozhnyy	ppl	62 35N	050 55E	RM
Zheleznogorsk	ppl	52 19N	035 12E	56,RM
Zheleznogorsk-Ilimskiy	ppl	56 34N	104 08E	57,RM
Zhëltyye Vody	ppl	48 21N	033 32E	RM
Zhëltyye Vody-Terny uranium deposit/ processing center	u/t	NA	NA	42,43
Zhetybay	oilf	43 20N	052 18E	21,27,66
Zhigalovo	ppl	54 48N	105 08E	RM
Zhigansk	ppl	66 45N	123 20E	RM
Zhigulevsk	oilf	53 27N	049 30E	20
Zhiloy	oilf	40 21N	050 35E	21
Zhitomir	ppl	50 15N	028 40E	79,RM
Zhitomirskaya Oblast'	admd	50 30N	028 30E	79
Zhokhova, Ostrov	isl	76 04N	152 40E	RM
Zima	ppl	53 55N	102 04E	57,RM
Zimniy	gasf	69 24N	085 08E	16
Zlatoust	ppl	55 10N	059 40E	56,RM
Zmiyëv (Gotval'd)	thep	NA	NA	49,67
Zol'noye	oilf	53 27N	049 46E	20
Zolotaya Gora	ppl	54 16N	126 38E	57,RM
Zuyevka	ppl	48 04N	038 15E	RM
Zuyevka	thep	NA	NA	49,67
Zvenigorodka coal deposit	coal	48 58N	031 10E	34
Zyryanka	ppl	65 45N	150 50E	RM
Zyryanka coal basin	coal	66 00N	146 00E	34,40
Zyryanka coal deposit	coal	66 00N	150 20E	34
Zyryanovsk	ppl	49 43N	084 20E	56,RM

Administrative Divisions

Novaya
Zemlya
(Arkhangel'skaya
Oblast')

Boundary   **Center**

——— Union republic (SSR)   ○

——— Autonomous republic (ASSR),   •
      oblast, or kray

- - - Autonomous oblast (AO) or
      autonomous okrug (AOk)

━━━ Economic region
      (lower map only)

*Note: An oblast is named only when its name differs
from that of its administrative center. Areas with no
oblast-level administrative divisions, where rayons
are under direct republic jurisdiction, are shown by
asterisks (∗).*

Murmansk

Nenetskiy AOk

Yamalo-
Nenetskiy
AOk

RUSSIAN SOVIET FEDERATIVE SOCIALIST REPUBLIC
(RSFSR)

Komi
ASSR

Khanty-Mansiyskiy
AOk

Krasnoyarsk

Tallinn   Petrozavodsk
ESTONIAN   Arkhangel'sk   Syktyvkar
SSR   Leningrad
Rīga   Tomsk
LATVIA   Pskov   Novgorod   Vologda   Komi-   Kemerovo
SSR   Permyatskiy
ingrad   Yaroslavl'   AOk   Sverdlovsk   Tyumen'   Severo-   Novosibirsk   Khakasskaya
(RSFSR) LITHUANIAN   Kalinin   Kostroma   Kirov   Kazakhstanskaya   AO
        SSR   Mariyskiy Udmurt-   Perm'   Oblast'   Barnaul
Vilnius   Vitebsk   Ivanovo   ASSR skaya   Kurgan   Omsk   Petropavlovsk   Altayskiy Kray   Gorno-
Grodno   Minsk   Smolensk Moscow Vladimir Yoshkar-Ola ASSR   Chelyabinsk   Altayskaya
BELORUSSIAN   Gor'kiy   Ustinov   Kokchetav   Pavlodar   AO
Brest   Mogilëv   Kaluga   Chuvash- Cheboksary Kazan'   Kustanay   Ust'-
ynskaya   Bryansk Tula skaya   Tatarskaya   Ufa   Bashkirskaya   Tselinograd   Semipalatinsk Kamenogorsk
blast'   Gomel'   Ryazan' Mo-dovskaya ASSR   ASSR   Vostochno-
L'vov   Rovno Zhitomir   Orël Lipetsk ASSR   Ul'yanovsk   Arkalyk   Karaganda   Kazakhstanskaya
gorod   Kiev   Chernigov   Tambov Penza Kuybyshev   Orenburg   Oblast'
Ivano- Ternopol' Vinnitsa Sumy Kursk   Saratov   Ural'sk   KAZAKH
Frankovsk   Poltava Voronezh Belgorod   Aktyubinsk Turgayskaya   Dzhezkazgan   SSR   Taldy-Kurgan
ernovtsy Khmel'nitskiy Cherkassy   Oblast'
arpatskaya   UKRAINIAN Kirovograd Dnepropetrovsk   Volgograd   Alma-Ata
Oblast'   SSR   Zaporozh'ye   Gur'yev   Przheval'sk
MOLDAVIAN SSR   Nikolayev   Rostov   Issyk-Kul'skaya
Kishinëv   Kherson   Donetsk   Elista   Astrakhan'   Kzyl-Orda   Oblast'
Odessa   Krasnodarskiy Kalmytskaya   Frunze
          Krymskaya   Kray Krasnodar ASSR   Dzhambul   Talas   Naryn
          Oblast'   Stavropol'   Mangyshlakskaya   Chimkent   KIRGHIZ
Simferopol'   1 Stavropol'skiy   Oblast'   Syrdar'inskaya Namangan SSR
                       Kray   Shevchenko   Oblast' Tashkent Andizhan
              Sukhumi 2 Nal'chik   Karakalpakskaya   Gulistan   Fergana Osh
          Abkhazskaya 3 Groznyy   Krasnovodsk   ASSR Nukus UZBEK   Dzhizak Leninabad Gorno-
          ASSR   4 Ordzhonikidze   Tashauz Urgench   SSR Samarkand   Badakhshanskaya AO
          GEORGIAN SSR 6 Makhachkala   Khorezmskaya   Navoi   Dushanbe TAJIK
          Batumi 7   Dagestanskaya   Oblast'   Bukhara   Karshi   TAJIK SSR
                         ASSR   Termez Kurgan-
          ARMENIAN 8   Ashkhabad   Tyube Kulyab
          SSR Yerevan   TURKMEN SSR   Chardzhou
                  AZERBAIJAN   Surkhandar'inskaya Oblast'
          9 SSR   Mary   Kashkadar'inskaya Oblast'
Nakhichevan' 8 Baku

ASSRs and AOs in the Caucasus

1. Adygeyskaya AO
2. Karachayevo-Cherkesskaya AO
3. Kabardino-Balkarskaya ASSR
4. Severo-Osetinskaya ASSR
5. Checheno-Ingushskaya ASSR
6. Yugo-Osetinskaya AO
7. Adzharskaya ASSR
8. Nagorno-Karabakhskaya AO
9. Nakhichevanskaya ASSR (Azerbaijan SSR)

Scale 1:20,000,000

0 ————————— 500 Kilometers

0 ————————— 500 Statute Miles

*Note: The Ukraine Economic Region is normally
divided into three regions—Donets-Dnepr, South,
and Southwest—by the Soviets. These regions have
been combined for simplification. Moldavian SSR is
not part of any economic region.*

Chukotskiy
AOk

Koryakskiy
AOk

BALTIC

NORTHWEST

BELORUSSIA

LDAVIAN
SSR   UKRAINE

Moscow

NORTHERN

CENTRAL

CENTRAL
CHERNOZEM

VOLGA-VYATKA

NORTH
CAUCASUS

VOLGA

URALS

Tyumen'

WEST

Taymyrskiy AOk

Yamalo-
Nenetskiy
AOk

Khanty-
Mansiyskiy
AOk

Evenkiyskiy
AOk

Yakutskaya
ASSR

Magadan

Kamchatskaya
Oblast'

FAR   EAST

Yakutsk

Petropavlovsk-
Kamchatskiy

Khabarovskiy
Kray

TRANS-
CAUCASUS

KAZAKHSTAN

SIBERIA

Omsk

Novosibirsk

Tomsk

EAST

Krasnoyarsk

Kemerovo

Barnaul
Altayskiy
Kray

Khakas-
skaya AO

Kyzyl

Tuvinskaya
ASSR

Gorno-Altayskaya
AO

Krasnoyarskiy

Kray

EAST

SIBERIA

Krasnoyarsk

Ust'-Ordynskiy
Buryatskiy AOk

Irkutsk

Ulan-
Ude

Buryatskaya
ASSR

Chita

Aginskiy
Buryatskiy
AOk

Blagoveshchensk

Amurskaya
Oblast'

Yevreyskaya
AO

Khabarovsk

Primorskiy
Kray

Vladivostok

Sakhalinskaya
Oblast'

Yuzhno-
Sakhalinsk

*Occupied by the
Soviet Union since
1945, claimed by
Japan.*

CENTRAL

ASIA

Scale 1:36,000,000

0 ———— 500 Kilometers

0 ———— 500 Statute Miles

79